Recognising wood rot and insect damage in buildings

A F Bravery BSc PhD DIC, R W Berry BSc,
J K Carey PhD DIC and D E Cooper

Building Research Establishment
Garston
Watford
WD2 7JR

Details of other BRE publications
can be obtained from:
BRE Bookshop
Building Research Establishment
Garston, Watford, WD2 7JR
Telephone 0923 664444

BR 232
ISBN 0 85125 535 3

First edition 1987
Second edition 1992

Contents

Foreword

Since the first edition of *Recognising wood rot and insect damage in buildings* was published in 1987, concern about the quality of the built environment and the use of natural resources has led to an emphasis on conservation, refurbishment and recycling of materials.

However, in order to conserve timber effectively, potentially harmful products sometimes have to be employed, with all the proper precautions. The starting point for treatment has to be the correct identification of the causes of timber damage since this should prevent application of the wrong pesticides and their unnecessary application to timbers which are showing only evidence of extinct insect damage, of harmless insects or of fungal damage which may be treated by drying out.

This book provides authoritative guidance on the identification of timber damage, drawing on over sixty years of experience. It has been written for surveyors, specialists in the remedial treatment of timber in buildings and those with an interest in the subject but without a background in biology. It will help them to make the right decisions about timber treatments.

The first edition was widely welcomed and I am sure that this new edition, in its very practical format, will be equally appreciated.

R G Courtney
Chief Executive
BRE

Acknowledgements

The authors would like to thank Ron Wilde (Wilde, Spooner, Raleigh), John Bricknell (formerly of Fosroc Timber Treatments), Ron Bonshor (former Head of BRE Advisory Service) and John Savory (former Head of Biodeterioration Section, BRE Princes Risborough Laboratory) for their advice on various parts of the book, and John Russell (BRE Photographic) who provided the photographs.

They also thank Peter Trotman (Head of BRE Advisory Service) for his comments on building inspection in this new edition.

Introduction

Wood is an inherently durable material which is resistant to most biological attack provided it remains dry. However, prolonged wetting leads to a risk of decay by wood-rotting fungi, though susceptibility varies according to the wood species[1]. Many types of fungi can be found in buildings, only some of which cause wood rot. Various insects, mostly beetles, also use wood as a food source, although high moisture content is not always a necessary condition for attack. Some fungi and insects require expensive remedial measures, while others do not require treatment at all, but correct identification is essential if the right treatment is to be given.

The purpose of this book is to enable recognition, on site, of the major wood-destroying fungi and insects found in building timbers. The information is given mainly in note form for easy reference, and is supported by flow charts (keys), colour photographs and line drawings to assist identification. Identification must often be undertaken by examination of the damaged wood alone and the information is presented with this in mind. However, additional advice is provided to help identification using any fungal or insect material found. Information is also given to distinguish the major wood-destroying species from harmless species which, though found in buildings, do not necessarily require treatment. Bibliographical references can be found on pages 112 and 113. The letter H in brackets, ie (H), indicates that the feature in question can be seen with a $\times$ 10 hand lens. In the keys the names of the rots and insects to be identified are shown in the boxes in bold type.

The parts of the book concerned with rots and similar conditions are identified by green-tinted page marginal strips, those for insects by brown tinted margins.

While the book includes most of the species associated with wood, and likely to be encountered in buildings, uncommon species which are rarely found are excluded. Should it prove to be impossible to identify any particular species using the advice given in this book, then the aid of an expert mycologist or entomologist must be sought.

Furthermore, some limited information is given on remedial treatments for fungal and insect attacks, but, as this is an area for specialist skills, detailed treatment procedures are not described. A separate book deals with these procedures[2].

Building inspection for fungal and insect attack

Pre-inspection procedure

- ❑ Establish with client and owner or occupier the extent of survey required and obtain written confirmation, particularly in relation to access to subfloor timbers and roof spaces.

- ❑ Establish as far as is possible with client and owner or occupier, the age and history of the building and any previous maintenance and repair work.

- ❑ Ensure that inspections for fungal and insect attack are carried out simultaneously.

Equipment

- ❑ Notebook, pens, pencils.

- ❑ Knife, bradawl or sharp screwdriver to probe for softening and 'brash' splintering.

- ❑ Hammer to 'sound' large-dimension timbers and detect internal decay or cavities.

- ❑ Hand lens giving a × 10 magnification.

- ❑ Moisture meter (conductivity type with insulated probes) and spare batteries.

- ❑ Mirror-on-a-stick and, possibly, borescope (a type of endoscope) to examine awkward areas.

- ❑ Rotary power and hand drills, and standard and masonry drill bits; ratchet and/or joist braces, and wood-boring bits and augers to assess damage within large-dimension timbers and to drill holes for the borescope if used.

- ❑ Camera to record conditions and faults; spare film and batteries.

- ❑ Robust torch with a strong beam, spare bulb and batteries.

- ❑ Small paint brush, forceps and containers to collect specimens; labels for specifying the contents of containers and where the specimens were found in the building.

- ❑ Binoculars to aid external survey.

- ❑ Bolster or crowbar to lift floor-boards; nails (cut and oval) to refix them.

- ❑ Compass to establish orientation of building.
- ❑ Ladder (3 metres, collapsible).
- ❑ Protective helmet, overalls and gloves.
- ❑ Filter mask (if required to inspect a dusty area or roof void containing, for example, glass fibre insulation).

External survey
Most cases of wood rot arise as a result of rainwater entering the fabric of the building or rising damp[3, 4, 5] so a careful external survey is the first priority. Make a simple plan of each floor and roof area of the building, and record on it the position and nature of all faults which may be causing wetting.

- ❑ Roof tiles or slates — missing or defective; pitch too shallow.
- ❑ Chimney — poorly capped or defective flashing.
- ❑ Eaves — inadequate ventilation (current Building Regulations require a continuous 10 mm slot, or equivalent, at the eaves).
- ❑ Valleys and gutters — blocked, leaking or sagging; gutters hung too low or tilted back.
- ❑ Flat roofs — damaged or failed waterproof membrane; sagging or ponding; split lead sheet; incorrect positioning of vapour control layer.
- ❑ Wall–roof junctions — defective flashing.
- ❑ Walls — rendering cracked or detached; cracked or flaking finish; brickwork crumbling; mortar deteriorating; algae (see page 43), moss or other plants growing, indicating dampness; uncapped projections (ie, string courses or cornices).
- ❑ Downpipes — blocked or broken, or of inadequate size; inadequate drainage to soakaway.
- ❑ Damp proof course (DPC) — missing or defective; bridged by soil or pathways.
- ❑ External joinery — cracked or flaking finish; cills without proper throating or drips, or blocked with paint.
- ❑ Air bricks — blocked or inadequate in size and number.
- ❑ Overflows — from cisterns or tanks splashing on walls.

Internal survey
Make a simple plan and elevations of the building layout and survey methodically, room by room, so that no rooms, built-in cupboards or ducting will be missed. Pay particular attention to timbers adjacent to actual, potential or previous points of moisture ingress and areas which may be subject to condensation, through faults in design or construction[6]. Examine internal plumbing for leakage particularly where concealed.

In each room, inspect all timbers and note the type of construction and the type of timber (hardwood or softwood). Measure and record the moisture contents and note all areas showing signs of dampness and therefore at risk from fungal attack (moisture contents over 20%). The following are areas particularly at risk.

- ❑ Skirtings on damp walls.
- ❑ Bearing ends of timbers in non-cavity walls.
- ❑ Wall plates near leaking gutters or below roof valleys.
- ❑ Roof timbers adjacent to damaged roof coverings or inadequate flashings.
- ❑ Joists of suspended floors where under floor ventilation is suspected as being inadequate.
- ❑ Timber lintels over openings in external walls — often buried behind plaster.
- ❑ Wall plates not on DPC on sleeper walls.
- ❑ Wood laid over solid floors, especially under impervious floor coverings.
- ❑ Cellars and basements.

Every effort should be made to examine all timbers at risk and a record should be made of all those which cannot be examined. Record the position, extent, type and state of activity of any wood rot or insect infestation found. Note evidence of past water ingress.

Symptoms of wood rot
- ❑ Loss in strength, softening or disintegration of the wood (probing with a sharp tool essential), splinters break off very short when raised by levering with probe.
- ❑ A hollow sound or similar change in note from larger members when struck with a hammer.

- ❑ Discolouration of the wood (lighter or darker than normal), often in patches or streaks.
- ❑ Fungal mycelium, strands or fruit-bodies.
- ❑ A distinctive 'mushroom' smell.
- ❑ Presence of certain wood-boring insects which only colonise decayed wood (see page 46).

Symptoms of insect infestation

- ❑ Holes in the wood surface — the holes usually have a characteristically clean sharp edge and need to be distinguished from holes made by nails and screws which leave a rounded edge; floor boards will often show holes for fixing floor coverings.
- ❑ Bore dust ejected through holes, forming small piles on or beneath timbers.
- ❑ Tunnels beneath the surface (exposed by wear on floorboards, or by probing).
- ❑ Larvae found by probing.
- ❑ Surface irregularities, usually bumps or corrugations, formed by pressure of bore dust beneath surface; may be detected by oblique lighting from torch or, if planed surface, by touch.

Significance of damage, repairs and treatments

- ❑ Assess state of activity of any fungal infection or insect infestation found. Where moisture contents are at or below 20%, wood rot will not be active. Freshly-cut emergence holes, piles of fresh bore dust around timbers or live larvae in probed wood suggest active infestation.
- ❑ Establish by thorough probing the extent of softening or powdering of timbers.
- ❑ Where serious weakening of structural timbers is suspected, in relation to their loading, seek the advice of a repair specialist or structural engineer[7].
- ❑ List all repairs required and recommended remedial treatments[8–16]. NOTE: there are specific regulations concerning insecticidal treatments to roof spaces known to be roosting sites for bats[17].

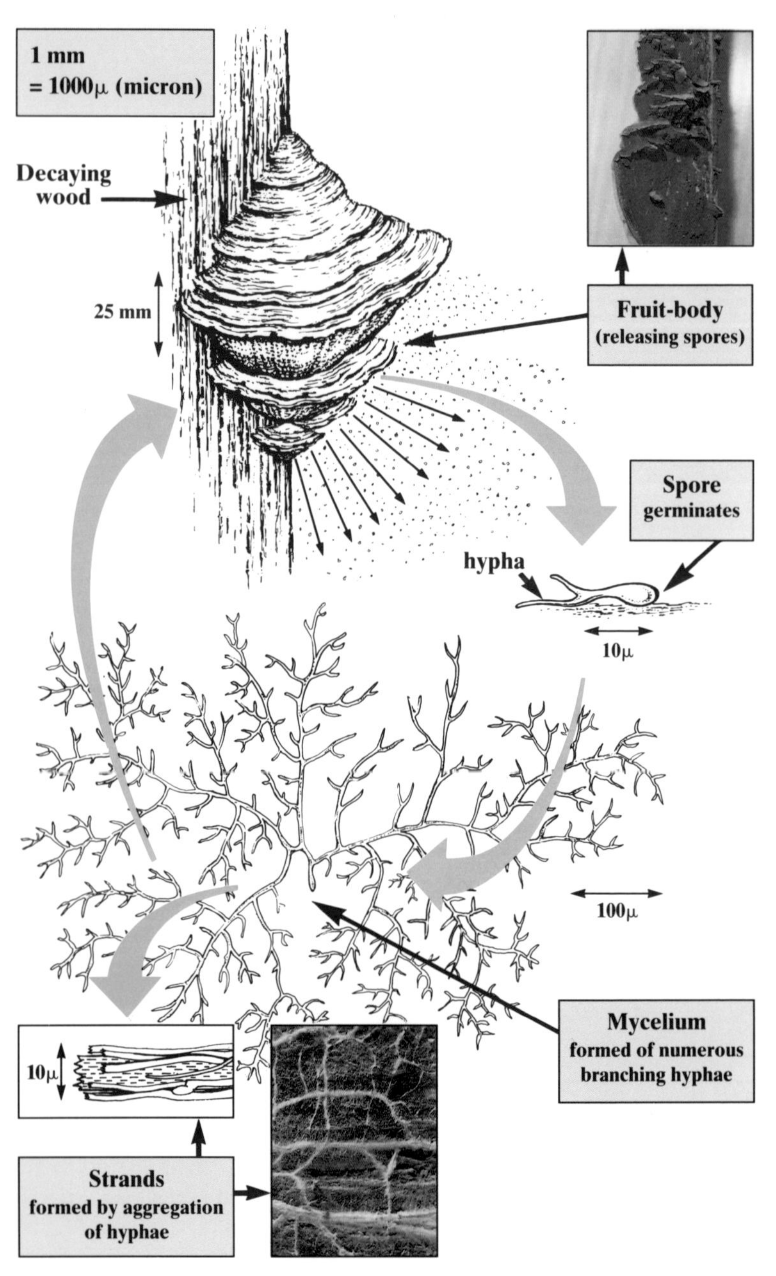

Life cycle of a typical wood-rotting fungus

Identification of wood-rotting fungi

Wood-rotting fungi obtain their food by breaking down wood cell walls, causing loss of strength. They cannot utilise wood at or below 20% moisture content and therefore do not occur in internal building timbers unless poor design or building faults have led to water entry or condensation.

Importance of identification

Not all fungi found in buildings cause wood rot (see page 8). However, the presence of any fungal growths indicates that damp conditions exist which are also suitable for the development of wood-rotting species. Remedial measures may be necessary to locate and remove the source of dampness, otherwise there is a risk that wood-rotting fungi could become established.

Wood-rotting fungi found in buildings can be divided into two major groups, according to their effect on wood.

White rots (see page 20) cause the wood to become lighter in colour and fibrous in texture without cross-cracking.

Brown rots (see pages 20 and 21) cause the wood to become darker in colour, and to crack along and across the grain. When dry, very decayed wood will crumble to dust.

Except for one brown rot, *Serpula lacrymans*, which is commonly called dry rot, all white rots and brown rots are referred to as wet rots.

It is not necessary to distinguish between the many species of wet rot which can be found in building timbers, since the same remedial measures are required for all of them[8].

S. lacrymans, the dry rot fungus, is significant for its ability to spread extensively behind plaster and through wall materials[9]. Successful remedial treatment may require more elaborate and sometimes very expensive measures[10].

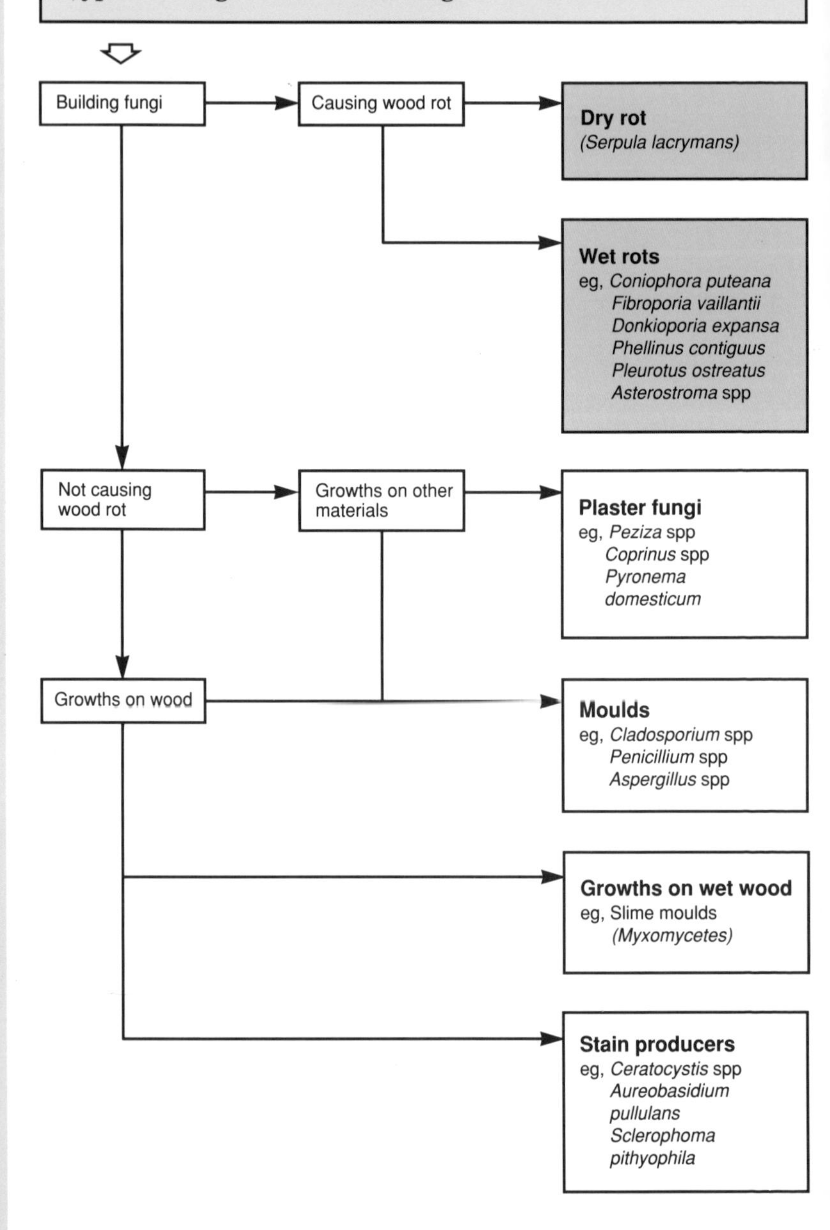

Types of fungi found in buildings
Building fungi
Causing wood rot
Dry rot
(Serpula lacrymans)
Wet rots
eg, Coniophora puteana
Fibroporia vaillantii
Donkioporia expansa
Phellinus contiguus
Pleurotus ostreatus
Asterostroma spp
Not causing wood rot
Growths on other materials
Plaster fungi
eg, Peziza spp
Coprinus spp
Pyronema domesticum
Growths on wood
Moulds
eg, Cladosporium spp
Penicillium spp
Aspergillus spp
Growths on wet wood
eg, Slime moulds
(Myxomycetes)
Stain producers
eg, Ceratocystis spp
Aureobasidium pullulans
Sclerophoma pithyophila

Key for identifying fungal growths in buildings

The word 'key' is used in the wood sciences to describe a set of instructions for identifying an organism. It is similar to 'decision tree' used in other fields of science and in business. An example of a simple key is shown on the opposite page.

The identification of fungal growths in buildings is not always easy, but various characteristics can help: fruit-bodies, strands, mycelium, condition and appearance of the wood.

Identification is easier if more than one of these characteristics is present. Often it is not possible to identify the organism if only one characteristic is found — for example it is not possible to recognise the fungus from the appearance of the wood alone.

Using the key (pages 10 to 14)
The key presented in the pages which follow includes only those fungi commonly found in buildings and is subdivided into the following sections:

Within each section a series of questions is asked concerning the appearance of the characteristic found (see Glossary, page 108, for definition of characteristics). If fruit-bodies are found, work through this section of the key until an identification is made. If fruit-bodies are not present or do not match any of the typical descriptions, turn to the next section (strands) and work through in a similar way. Continue through each section until you have established whether or not identification is possible. If a provisional identification is made using the first or second characteristic, work through the other sections also as this may help to confirm identification. Once this is made, turn to the page giving more detailed information on the fungus for further confirmation.

It cannot be assumed that the key will provide an unequivocal answer; it can only be an aid to identification because of the extent of natural variations in colour and form which occur. Sometimes it may not be possible to identify the fungus using the key and the aid of an expert in mycological identification should be sought. However, in practice it is normally only essential to establish whether the fungus is dry rot, a wet rot or a non-wood-rotting species.

Colour coded boxes are used within the key, and in the pages which follow it, to characterise identified fungi:

wood-rotting fungus

non-wood-rotting fungus

Key for identifying fungal growths in buildings
Fruit-bodies

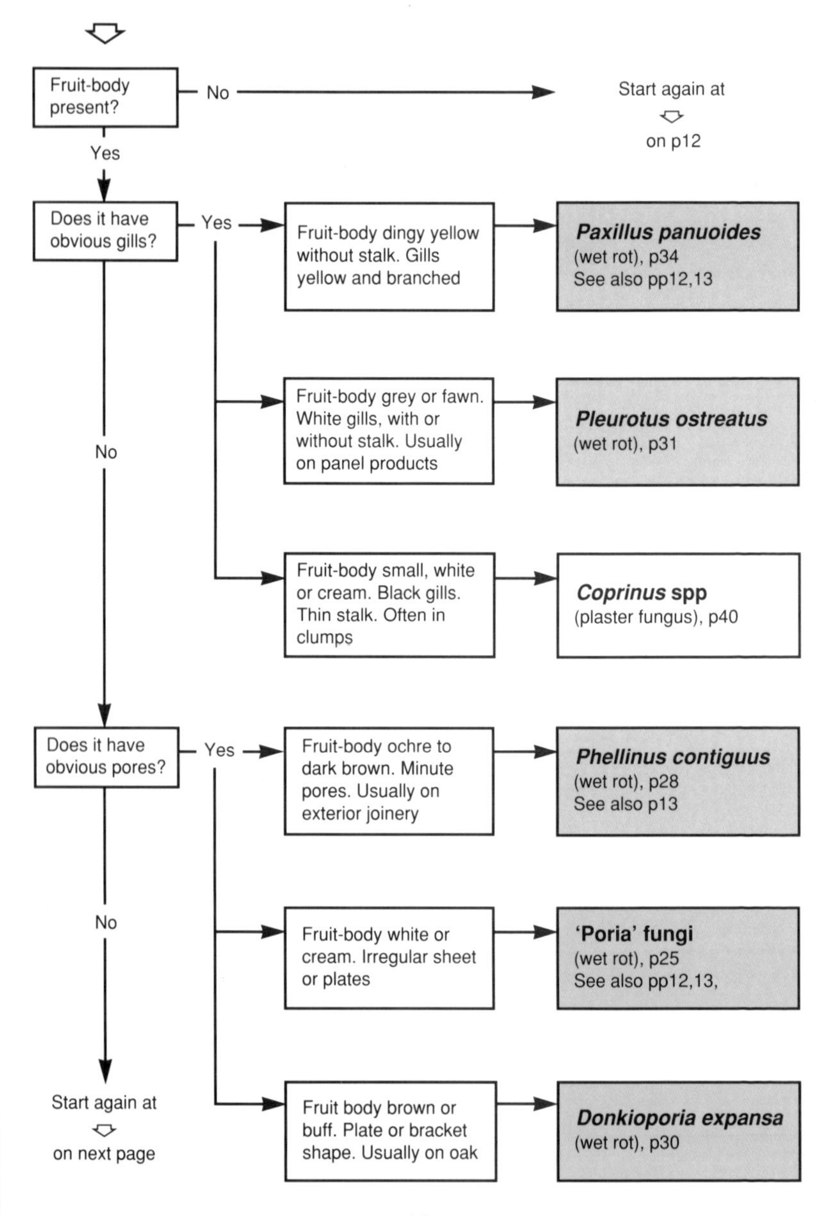

Key for identifying fungal growths in buildings

Fruit-bodies (continued)

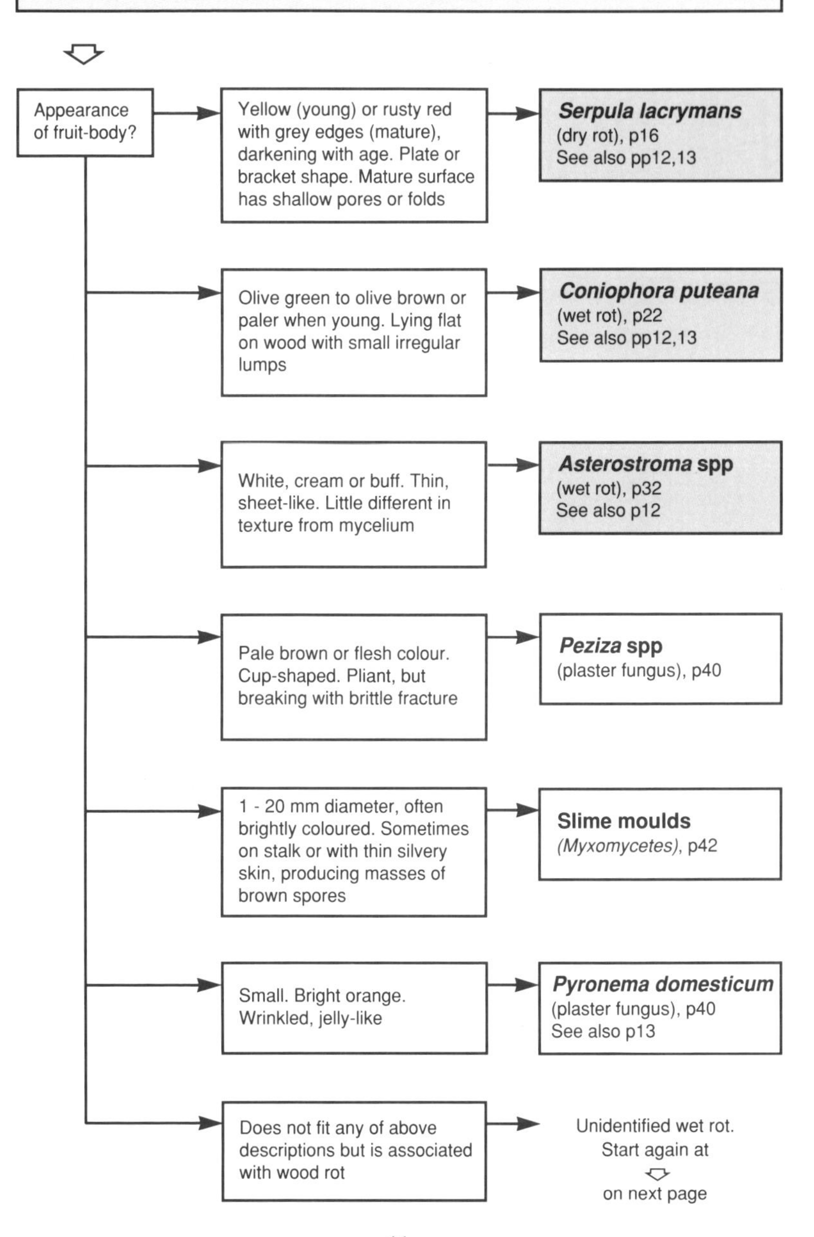

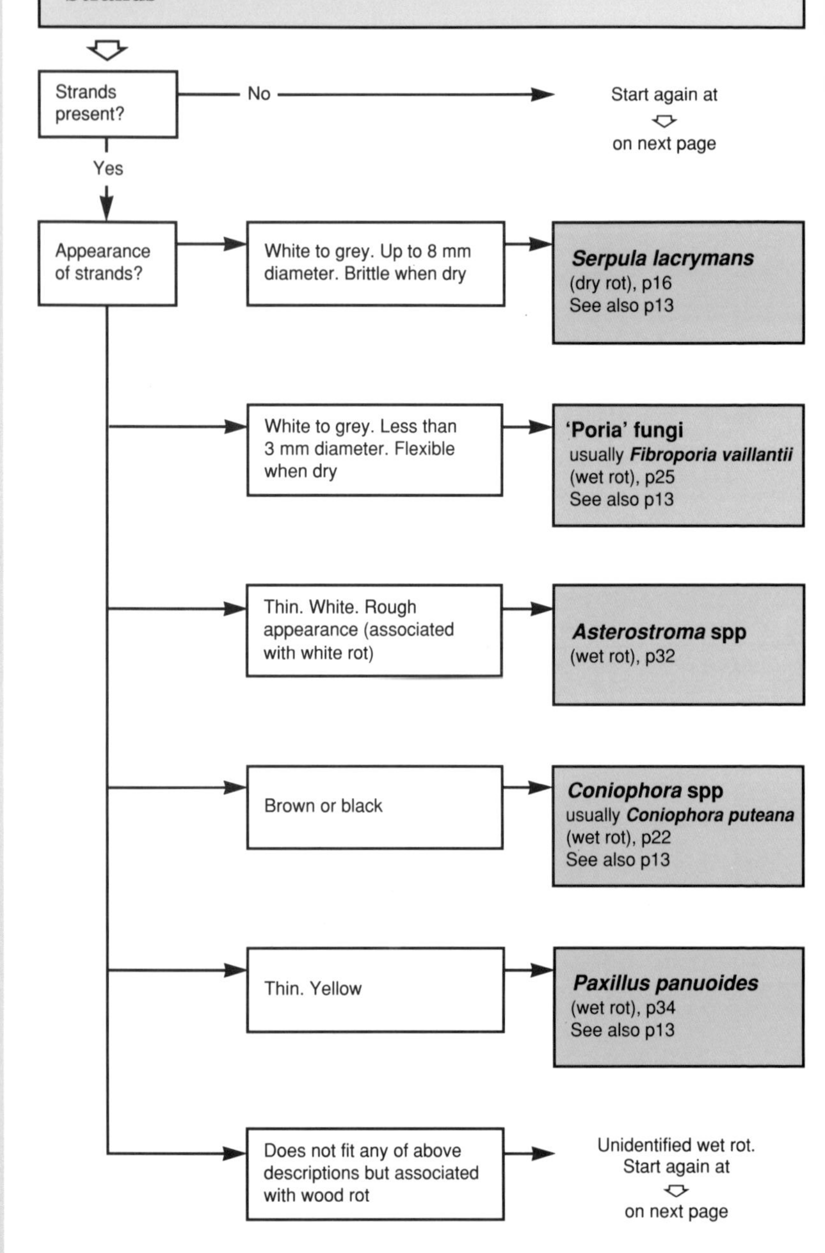

Key for identifying fungal growths in buildings
Strands
Strands present?
No
Start again at
on next page
Yes
Appearance of strands?
White to grey. Up to 8 mm diameter. Brittle when dry
Serpula lacrymans (dry rot), p16 See also p13
White to grey. Less than 3 mm diameter. Flexible when dry
'Poria' fungi usually *Fibroporia vaillantii* (wet rot), p25 See also p13
Thin. White. Rough appearance (associated with white rot)
Asterostroma spp (wet rot), p32
Brown or black
Coniophora spp usually *Coniophora puteana* (wet rot), p22 See also p13
Thin. Yellow
Paxillus panuoides (wet rot), p34 See also p13
Does not fit any of above descriptions but associated with wood rot
Unidentified wet rot. Start again at
on next page

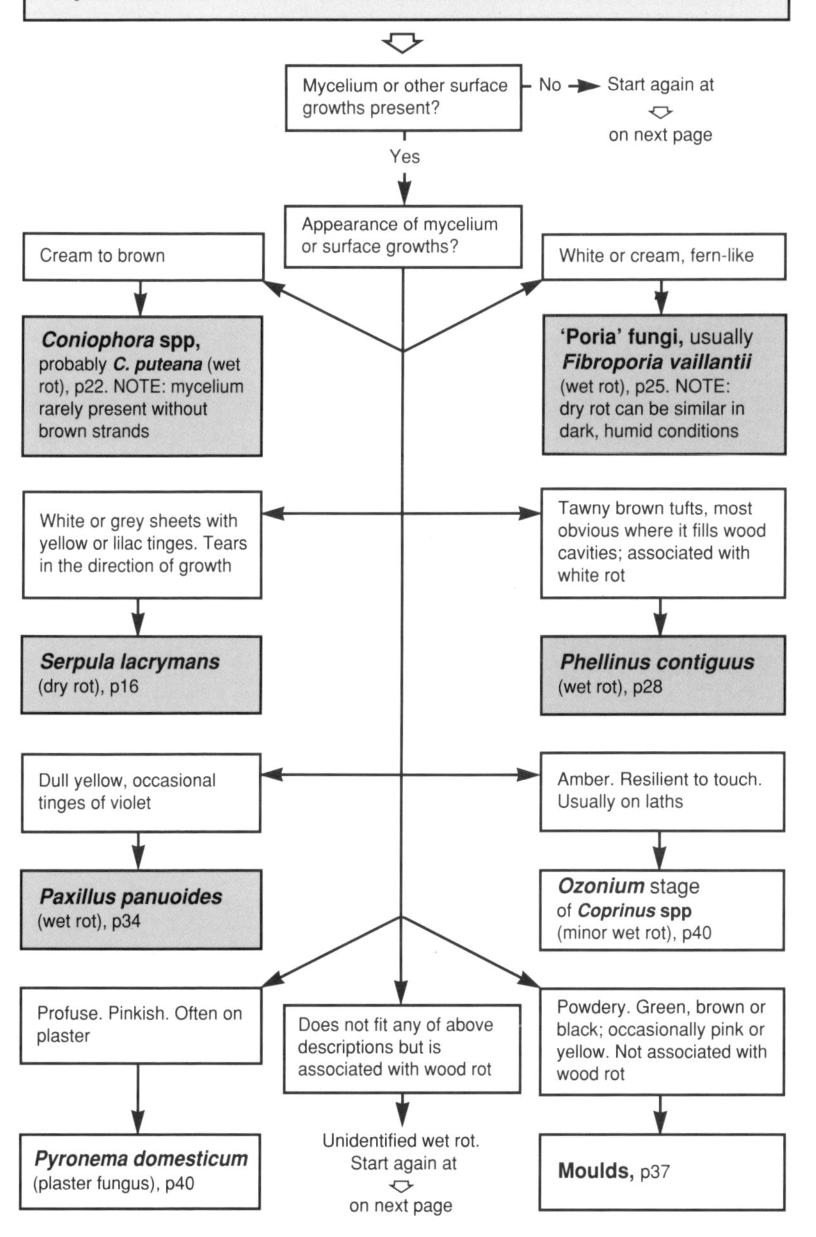

Key for identifying fungal growths in buildings
Mycelium
Mycelium or other surface growths present?
No
Start again at
on next page
Yes
Appearance of mycelium or surface growths?
Cream to brown
Coniophora spp, probably C. puteana (wet rot), p22. NOTE: mycelium rarely present without brown strands
White or cream, fern-like
'Poria' fungi, usually Fibroporia vaillantii (wet rot), p25. NOTE: dry rot can be similar in dark, humid conditions
White or grey sheets with yellow or lilac tinges. Tears in the direction of growth
Serpula lacrymans (dry rot), p16
Tawny brown tufts, most obvious where it fills wood cavities; associated with white rot
Phellinus contiguus (wet rot), p28
Dull yellow, occasional tinges of violet
Paxillus panuoides (wet rot), p34
Amber. Resilient to touch. Usually on laths
Ozonium stage of Coprinus spp (minor wet rot), p40
Profuse. Pinkish. Often on plaster
Pyronema domesticum (plaster fungus), p40
Does not fit any of above descriptions but is associated with wood rot
Unidentified wet rot.
Start again at
on next page
Powdery. Green, brown or black; occasionally pink or yellow. Not associated with wood rot
Moulds, p37

Key for identifying fungal growths in buildings

Appearance of the wood

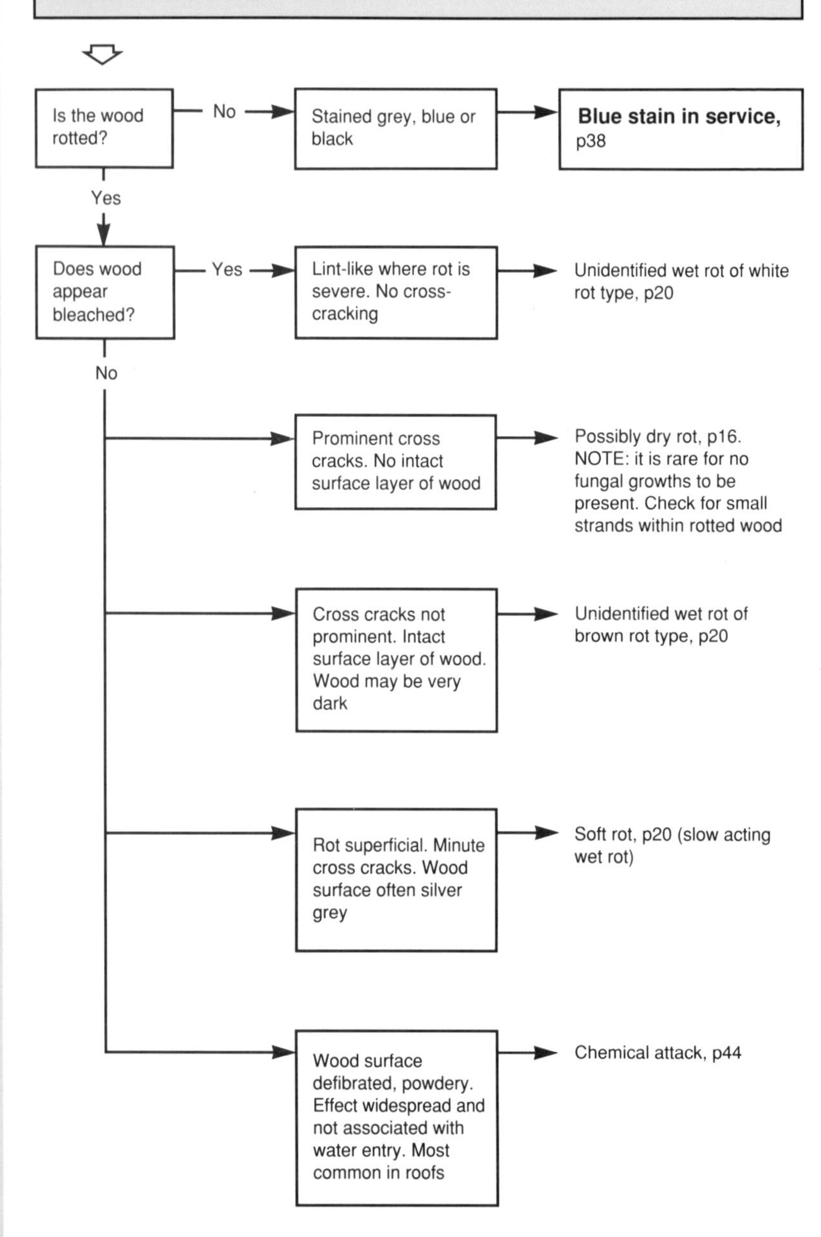

Wood-rotting fungi

This part of the book includes the following:

Dry rot: *Serpula lacrymans*

Remedial treatment of dry rot

Wet rots

Wet rot: *Coniophora puteana* (cellar fungus)
'Poria' fungi
Phellinus contiguus
Donkioporia expansa
Pleurotus ostreatus (oyster fungus)
Asterostroma spp
Paxillus panuoides

Remedial treatment of wet rot

Dry rot

Latin name: *Serpula lacrymans*
Common name: dry rot fungus

Habitat Mostly softwoods.

General information Major building decay fungus often causing extensive damage. A brown rot which typically occurs on wood embedded in, or in contact with, wet brickwork. Sensitive to high temperatures (over 25°C) and drying, and therefore rarely found on exposed timbers or in situations where fluctuating conditions are likely (eg, well ventilated subfloors and roofing timbers). Able to grow through bricks and mortar, though cannot feed on these. Strands can transport moisture from damp areas, allowing spread of the fungus to dry wood in unventilated conditions. Appearance of fruit-body may be first indication of outbreak.

Damage characteristics Decayed wood has dull brown colour, typically with deep cracks along and across the grain. Light in weight and crumbles between fingers. No skin of sound wood.

Dry rot — typical damage

Fungal characteristics:
Mycelium Silky white sheets or cotton wool-like white cushions with patches of lemon yellow or lilac tinges where exposed to light. In less humid conditions, forms thin, felted grey skin. During active growth the advancing hyphal edge forms a silky fringe. Tears in direction of growth.
Strands White to grey, branching, sometimes as thick as a pencil. Brittle when dry.
Fruit-body Usually on wood–wall joint, rare on exterior of building. Tough, fleshy, pancake or bracket-shaped. Centre is yellow ochre when young, darkening to rusty red when mature owing to spore production. Covered with shallow pores or folds. Edges white or grey.
Spores Profuse and may settle as fine layer of reddish brown dust on horizontal surfaces.

Dry rot — fruit-body in the corner of ceiling (note spores collected on cobwebs)

Dry rot — sheets of mycelium exposed by removal of timber wall panelling. (Inset photograph shows enlargement of grey strands in bottom right hand portion of mycelium)

Remedial treatment of dry rot[2, 9, 10]

- Establish the size and significance of the attack. In particular, if structural timbers are affected, carry out or arrange for a full structural survey to determine whether structural repairs are necessary and, if they are, take appropriate steps to secure structural integrity[7].

- Locate and eliminate sources of moisture.

- Promote rapid drying of the structure.

- Remove all rotted wood, cutting away timber approximately 300 – 450 mm from the last evidence of fungus or rot.

- Contain the fungus within the wall using preservatives in cases where drying will be delayed.

- In replacement work, use preservative-treated timbers.

- Treat remaining sound timbers which are at risk with preservative (minimum two full brush coats).

- Introduce support measures (such as ventilation pathways between sound timber and wet brickwork, or, where ventilation is not possible, providing a barrier such as a damp proof membrane or joist-hangers between timber and wet brickwork).

- Do not retain timber which has been infected by dry rot without seeking expert advice. There is always some risk in retaining infected wood which can be minimised by preservative treatment and subsequent inspection.

Wet rots

There are many fungal species causing wet rot and the same remedial measures are required for all of them. They may cause a darkening of the timber (brown rot) or bleaching (white rot). Some types are only rarely found in buildings; the following pages give information on those species most commonly found or most easily identified. In many cases it is not possible to identify the species responsible.

Soft rot can be regarded as a superficial form of wet rot. It is more usually found on timber in ground contact.

Typical white rot damage to timber

Typical brown rot damage to timber

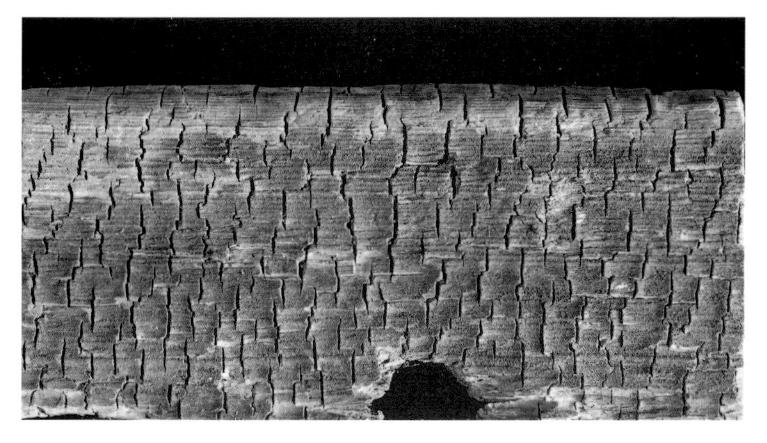

Typical soft rot damage to timber

Wet rot

Latin name: *Coniophora puteana*
Common name: cellar fungus
Type of decay: brown rot

Habitat Softwoods and hardwoods

General information Commonest cause of decay in woodwork which has become soaked by water leakage.

Damage characteristics Wood darkens with cracks along and across grain, but usually less deep than those caused by *Serpula lacrymans*. Where conditions cause drying of the wood surface, an apparently sound skin of timber often remains which may crack longitudinally as the decay progresses beneath. Freshly colonised wood usually shows a yellow discolouration.

Coniophora puteana — freshly colonised wood showing distinctive yellow colouring as compared to lighter coloured areas of unaffected wood

Fungal characteristics:

Mycelium Only present in conditions of high humidity and rarely without brown strands. Cream to brownish in colour; off-white under impervious floor coverings. May spread superficially over damp plaster or brickwork.

Strands Thin, usually brown or black, though yellowish when young.

Fruit-body Rare in buildings. Thin, lying flat on substrate and with small irregular lumps. Olive green to olive brown with cream margin; paler when young.

Coniophora puteana — longer term damage showing typical cuboidal cracking

Coniophora puteana — strands

Coniophora puteana — fruit-bodies

Wet rot

Latin names: 'Poria' fungi including *Amyloporia xantha*, *Fibroporia vaillantii* and *Poria placenta*
Other names: *F. vaillantii* is also referred to as white pore fungus or mine fungus
Type of decay: brown rot

Habitat Softwoods

General information This group of wet rots is a common cause of damage in damp woodwork in buildings, frequently in areas of higher temperature. Damage can be extensive, particularly where caused by *Fibroporia vaillantii*.

Damage characteristics Resembles *Serpula lacrymans*. Wood breaks up into cuboidal pieces but decayed wood is lighter in colour and cracks are not usually as deep as those caused by *S. lacrymans*.

Fungal characteristics:
Mycelium White or cream sheets or fern-like growths. May discolour brown on contact with iron.
Strands Seldom thicker than twine, white to cream, remaining flexible when dry (only well developed in *F. vaillantii*).
Fruit-body Irregular lumpy sheets or plates, white or cream to pale yellow. Spore-bearing surface white to pale yellow with numerous minute pores, occasionally also with pink patches (*Poria placenta* only).

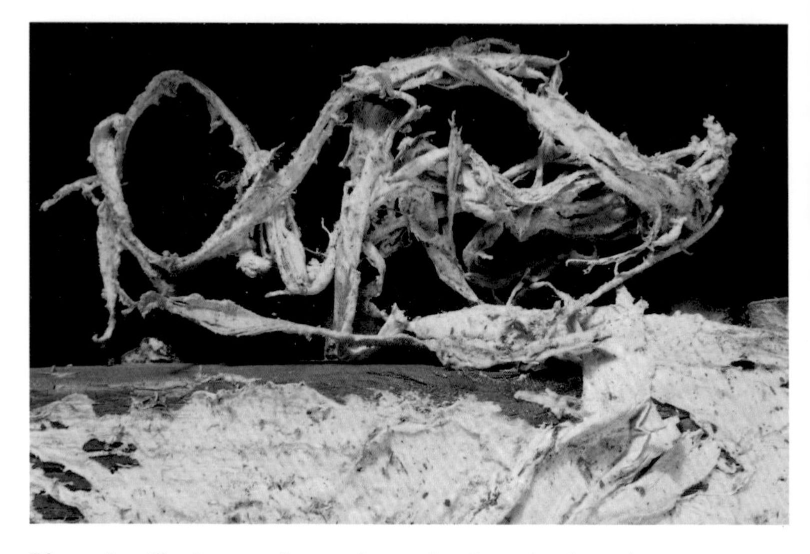

Fibroporia vaillantii — mycelium on the wood, and associated strands

Fibroporia vaillantii — fruit-body

Poria placenta — fruit-body

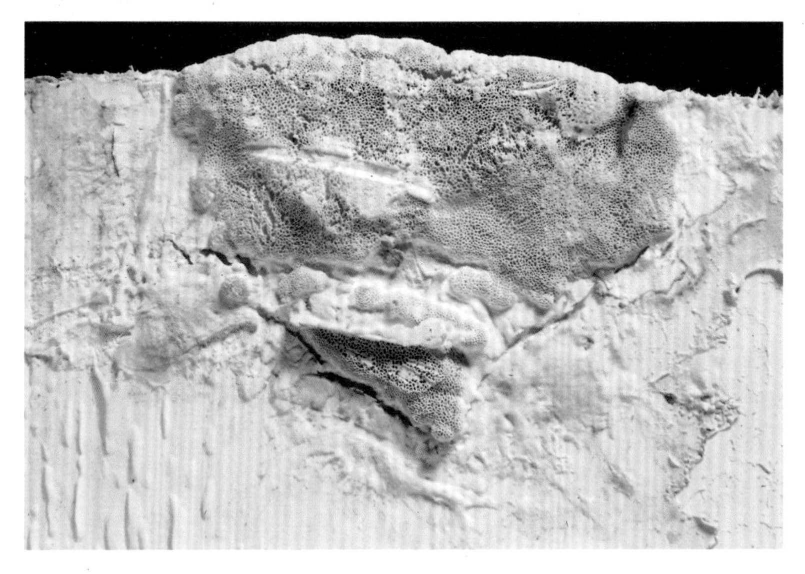

Amyloporia xantha — fruit-body

Wet rot

Latin name: *Phellinus contiguus*
Type of decay: white rot

Habitat Softwoods and hardwoods. Common on external joinery.

Damage characteristics Wood bleaches and eventually develops stringy, fibrous appearance. No cuboidal cracking. Does not crumble.

Fungal characteristics:
Mycelium Tawny brown tufts which can be found around fruit-body or in crevices in the wood.
Strands None.
Fruit-body Occasionally found. Tough, elongated, ochre to dark brown in colour. Covered in minute pores.

Phellinus contiguus — fruit-body and damaged wood

Phellinus contiguus — damaged wood with tufts of tawny brown mycelium (shown about 5 times actual size)

Wet rot

Latin name: *Donkioporia expansa*
Type of decay: white rot

Habitat Hardwoods, particularly oak, though may spread to adjacent softwoods.

General information Common on timbers where there has been persistent water leakage. Can cause more extensive damage to oak than any other fungus. Often found at ends of beams embedded in damp walls. Damage may be confined to interior of beam and not noticed until fruit-bodies appear. Deathwatch beetle attack (see page 65) is often associated with this fungus .

Damage characteristics Wood becomes bleached and is reduced to lint-like consistency leaving stringy white fibres. Decayed wood easily crushed but does not crumble.

Fungal characteristics:
Mycelium Yellow to red-brown thick felted growth, often shaped to contours of wood. Exudes drops of yellowish-brown liquid.
Strands None.
Fruit-body Thin and leathery, or thick, hard and woody; plate or bracket-shaped. Brown or buff coloured. Spore bearing surface is cinnamon brown or fawn coloured with numerous minute pores. Often several pore layers present.

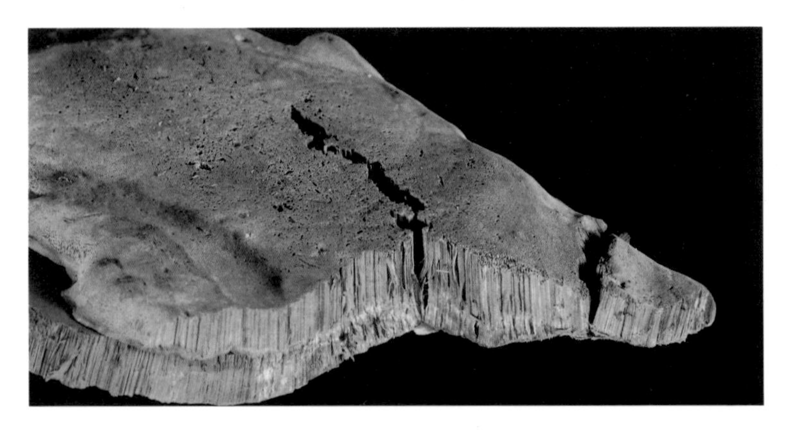

Donkioporia expansa — fruit-body (separated from wood)

Wet rot

Latin name: *Pleurotus ostreatus*
Common name: oyster fungus
Type of decay: white rot

Habitat and general information Generally found on broad-leaved trees. Occasionally found in buildings, usually as cause of decay in panel products.

Damage characteristics Panels lighten in colour. In particleboards, chips tend to separate.

Fungal characteristics:
Mycelium Whitish, woolly mat.
Strands None.
Fruit-body Grey or fawn mushroom-type with whitish, plate-like gills beneath, with or without stalk. Stalk, if present, not central.

Pleurotus ostreatus — fruit-bodies

Wet rot

Latin name: *Asterostroma* spp
Type of decay: white rot

Habitat and general information Softwoods. Usually found on joinery (eg, skirting boards). Often limited in extent of spread.

Damage characteristics Wood becomes bleached and develops stringy, fibrous appearance. No cuboidal cracking. Does not crumble.

Fungal characteristics:
Mycelium White, cream or buff sheets (not always present).
Strands Thin, white, with rough appearance. Remain flexible when dry. Sometimes can cross masonry over long distances. Small brown strands are often present next to the fruit-body.
Fruit-body Thin, sheet-like, hardly distinguishable from mycelium. No pores. May be found on masonry.

Asterostroma — strands on damaged wood

Asterostroma sp — fruit-body

Wet rot

Latin name: *Paxillus panuoides*
Type of decay: brown rot

Habitat and general information Softwoods. Prefers very damp situations.

Damage characteristics Initially a vivid yellow discolouration appears wherever mycelium is present. In an advanced stage the decayed wood becomes soft and cheesy, and, on drying, deep longitudinal fissures and some fine cross-cracks appear.

Fungal characteristics:
Mycelium Soft; hairy or woolly. Dull yellow with occasional tinges of violet.
Strands Thin, colour as mycelium. Do not darken with age.
Fruit-body Dingy yellow. Fan or funnel-shaped, without stalk. Gills yellow and branch frequently.

Paxillus panuoides — mycelium and strands on damaged wood; fruit-bodies shown detached

Remedial treatment of wet rot[2,8]

- ❑ Establish the size and significance of the attack. In particular, if structural timbers are affected, carry out or arrange for a full structural survey to determine whether structural repairs are necessary and, if they are, take appropriate steps to secure structural integrity[7].
- ❑ Locate and eliminate sources of moisture.
- ❑ Promote rapid drying of the structure.
- ❑ Remove rotted wood; apply localised preservative treatment only to timbers which are likely to remain damp for long periods.
- ❑ In replacement work, use preservative-treated timbers.
- ❑ Introduce support measures (such as ventilation pathways between sound timber and wet brickwork, or, where ventilation is not possible, providing a barrier such as a damp proof membrane or joist-hangers between timber and wet brickwork).

Non-wood-rotting fungi

This part of the book includes the following:

Moulds

Blue stain in service

Plaster fungi: *Coprinus* spp; *Peziza* spp; *Pyronema domesticum*

Slime moulds

Moulds

Latin names: many types, commonly *Penicillium* spp, *Aspergillus* spp and *Cladosporium* spp (*Cladosporium* spp also cause blue stain in service when growing on wood)

Habitat and general information Surface of damp wood, plaster, wallpaper or paint. Feed on free sugars in wood or surface deposits of detritus.

Fungal characteristics Surface growths usually downy and produce masses of powdery spores. Various colours, depending on species — black, brown, green, occasionally pink or yellow. Some are rusty red and may be mistaken for spores of *Serpula lacrymans*. Some produce a fluffy mass of white growth which may also be mistaken for dry rot mycelial growth.

Remedial treatment[11] Ventilate to encourage drying and disperse airborne spores. Remove surface spores with a damp cloth and vacuum cleaner. Clean surfaces with a fungicidal wash which will also prevent re-growth during drying-out. Remove badly damaged decorations. Locate and remove source of dampness. Continue with ventilation and heating to ensure drying out. Do not redecorate until surfaces are thoroughly dried out. Where damp conditions are likely to remain, only effective fungicidal paints should be used when redecorating.

Mould growth

Blue stain in service

Latin names: many species, commonly *Aureobasidium pullulans*, *Sclerophoma pithyophila*, *Diplodia* spp, *Cladosporium* spp
(Blue stain in service is often confused with 'sap stain' or 'blue stain' of freshly felled logs or fresh sawn timber, but these latter fungi are mostly from different genera, eg *Ceratocystis*, although causing a blue colour which is still detectable in service.)

Habitat and general information The sapwood cells of moist wood but mainly ray cells. Cannot grow in waterlogged wood or at or below 20% moisture content. Fungal hyphae penetrate cell walls and feed on cell contents but not on wood substance.

Damage characteristics Disfigurement of the wood and especially of clear finishes. Early failure of surface coatings caused by rupture by the fruit-bodies. NOTE: discolouration caused by sap stain which has occurred in the log may still be detectable after drying and conversion of the timber, but this will only affect the aesthetic value of the wood. Damage to coatings will only occur through the growth of blue stain in service.

Fungal characteristics Black, blue-black or grey streaks and patches on and in wood or coating. Sometimes dark hyphae and fruit-bodies are present (tiny nodular structures erupting through the coating). Staining penetrates deeply and often cannot be removed by surface planing.

Remedial treatment Exterior timbers only. Remove damaged surface coatings, dry the timber and treat with a wood preservative containing an additive specifically active against these fungi. Apply new surface coating.

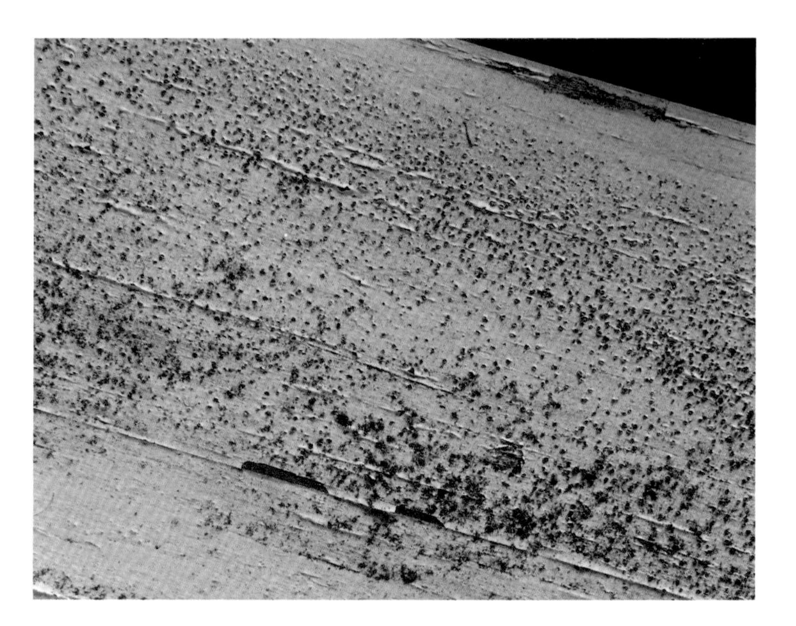

Blue stain in service causing damage to paint

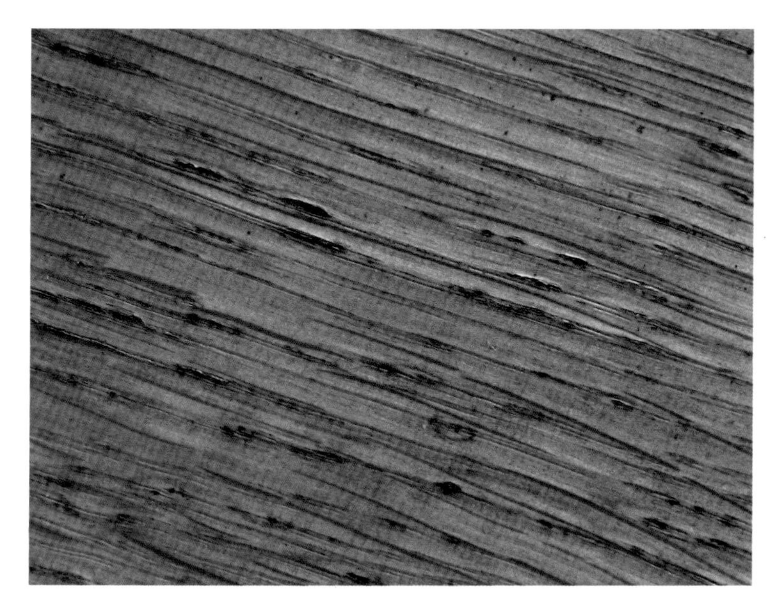

Blue stain in service causing damage to natural finish

Plaster fungi

Latin names: *Coprinus* spp; *Peziza* spp; *Pyronema domesticum*
Common names: respectively inkcap; elf cup; no common name

Habitat and general information Damp brickwork or plaster. Feed on surface detritus or on organic material included in walls (eg, bituminised felt DPCs or hair contained in old plasters).

Fungal characteristics Produce large fruit-bodies, or mycelial growths which may be mistaken for those of wood-rotting fungi.
Coprinus spp: small white or cream mushroom-type fruit-body with black gills and thin stalk. Often in clumps. Produces black spores often deposited as a 'spore print' when fruit-body matures before it shrivels and collapses. In vegetative non-fruiting *Ozonium* stage of life cycle, may cause some decay to sapwood of hardwood (eg, to split laths).
Peziza spp: small, pale brown or flesh-coloured cup-shaped fruit-body without stalk. Up to 50 mm wide. Often in clumps. Pliant when fresh but breaks easily with brittle fractures when stressed between fingers. Hard when dry.
Pyronema domesticum: fruit-body small, bright orange, wrinkled, jelly-like. Mycelium profuse, pinkish but otherwise resembling that of *Serpula lacrymans*. Commonly occurs following fires.

Remedial treatment Locate and remove source of dampness.

Coprinus sp — fruit-bodies

Peziza sp — fruit-bodies

Pyronema domesticum — fruit-body (shown about 4 times actual size) growing on flakes of white paint

Slime moulds

Latin names: many types known collectively as *Myxomycetes*

Habitat and general information Damp wood, usually exterior joinery. Feed on bacteria within wood and only become visible when they produce fruit-bodies on the surface.

Fungal characteristics (fruit-bodies) 1 – 20 mm in diameter, variable in appearance, often brightly coloured, sometimes on stalks or with a thin silvery skin. All produce masses of brown spores.

Remedial treatment[11] Locate and remove source of dampness. Remove surface growths.

Myxomycetes — spore dust from ruptured fruit-bodies on wood and (inset) one example of the variable fruit-bodies

Algal growths

Latin names: many types, commonly *Pleurococcus* spp, *Stichococcus bacillaris* and *Nostoc commune*

Habitat and general information External damp surfaces. Common on masonry walls, roof coverings, timber and paint. Require exposure to sunlight for growth. Encouraged by rough-textured damp surfaces which allow accumulation of organic nutrient-containing detritus.

Identifying characteristics The algal coating on an affected surface initially has a bright green colour. This coating subsequently thickens and changes to a green slime. Drying may cause it to die, in which case it shows a blackened or dirty appearance. In the long term the algal growth may progress to a lichen stage in which it develops crust-like patches of varying colours.

Remedial treatment[18] Localised areas of algae indicate some form of water flow, possibly due to leaking rainwater goods or overflows, or the absence of drip channels in window cills. These must be rectified. Generalised growth over wall or room surfaces indicates high levels of exposure to driving rain, a porous surface, or a surface with an inadequate slope to ensure rapid drainage. Periodic removal of growths by wire-brushing and application of a masonry biocide or algicidal paint to restrict re-colonisation is appropriate. NOTE: algal growths on wall surfaces are an indication of possible fungal decay problems in associated internal timbers (eg, joist ends).

Algal growth resulting from overflowing hopper

Chemical attack of wood

Chemicals can cause damage which may be mistaken for attack by wood-rotting fungi. The damage can be due to acid or alkaline chemicals, commonly from industrial atmospheric pollution, leaking flues or salts eluting from tiles or lime mortar torching; it may be associated with corrosion of metal fastenings, often called 'nail sickness'. The most common form is sulphate attack of roof timbers; the wood becomes defibrated and may be covered with powdery crystals — not unlike fungus mycelium — which crumble when touched or brushed. The attack is usually only superficial but it may be widespread.

Chemical damage to wood (about 80% of actual size)

Identification of wood-boring insects

A number of insects, mainly beetles, are able to use wood as a food source and some of them can cause serious damage to building timbers. These insects all have fairly similar life cycles, although there are variations in the length of each stage in the life cycle, the type of wood attacked, and the extent and type of damage caused.

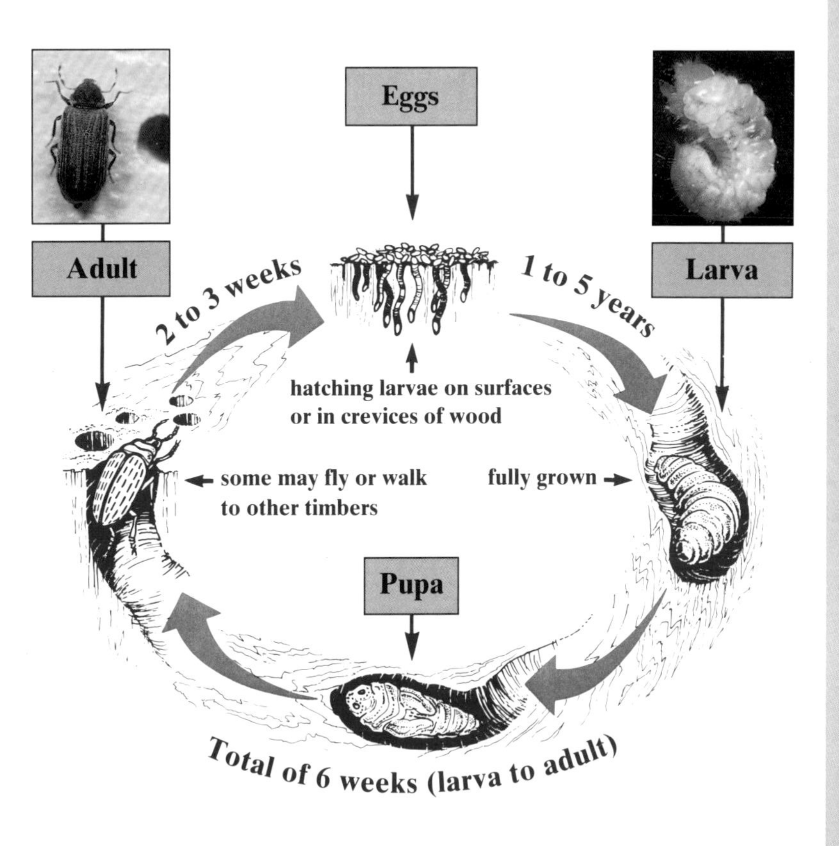

Life cycle of a typical wood-boring insect

Importance of identification

The presence of damage caused by wood-boring insects does not always indicate a need for remedial treatment[14–16, 19], but correct identification is essential if the right treatment is to be selected. Wood-boring insects commonly found in building timbers fall into one of three categories according to the treatment normally required.

Damage category	Remedial measures
A Insecticidal treatment usually needed	A few insects are a primary cause of serious damage and these require an insecticidal treatment; with the exception of the deathwatch beetle they all attack sound wood. Some can cause structural damage (eg, deathwatch beetle and house longhorn beetle) and with these a structural survey may be necessary.

NOTE: sometimes infestations by insects within this category may have died out naturally or been killed by the actions of parasites. Inactive infestations do not require treatment.

Damage category	Remedial measures
B Treatment necessary only to control associated wood rot	Some insects are only able to feed on damp wood, rotted by fungi. Since they cannot attack sound dry wood, further infestation by these insects is prevented by the remedial measures necessary to control wood rot.
C No treatment needed	Timber damaged by insects which attack green or partially dry timber may be incorporated into buildings, but the insects have usually been killed during drying and therefore no remedial treatment is necessary. Insects which normally feed on other materials, only boring into wood to make short refuge tunnels, are also included in this category. These insects also do not require insecticidal treatment of the wood since removal of the food source will prevent further damage.

The actual dimensions of adult insects and larvae are given in the detailed descriptions and are also shown against diagrams. These dimensions represent body length excluding appendages such as legs and antennae; for larvae which are generally curved, the length given is that of the straightened body.

Recommendations for treatments for the different wood-boring insects are given within the details for each insect type. Treatment procedures are described on page 100.

Keys for identifying wood-boring insects

The following pages contain a key to the identification of wood-boring insects and a further key for identifying larvae likely to be encountered in buildings. (The word 'key' is used in the wood sciences to describe a set of instructions for identifying an organism. It is similar to 'decision tree' used in other fields of science and in business.)

Adult wood-boring insects are normally found only at certain times of the year and are rarely seen. However, a range of other insects may be found in buildings which can be confused with the adults of wood-boring types and normally expert knowledge is needed to distinguish between them. Therefore no general key to the identification of adult insects is provided, but the pages giving further information on individual insects include descriptions of the adults.

Using the keys (pages 49 to 55)

For the damage key, it is necessary to turn to the page with the size and shape of the emergence hole similar to the damage found (pages 49 to 52 inclusive); for the larval stage, start at page 53. Both keys are used in the same way: simply work through, answering each question until a provisional identification is made. Turn to the page providing detailed information on the insect for confirmation. If the information does not confirm the identification, check back through the key in case a question was incorrectly answered.

If the information on damage characteristics confirms the identification, but adult insects are found which do not match the description provided, these may be non-wood-boring insects which have entered the building by chance (see pages 101 to 103).

In both the keys and the pages of descriptions of individual insects, colour coded boxes are used:

Box	Meaning
(dark shaded box)	Damage category A — insecticidal treatment usually needed
(light shaded box)	Damage category B — treatment necessary only to control associated wood rot
(white box)	Damage category C — no treatment needed

The symbol (H) indicates a feature identifiable with a × 10 hand lens.

Damage or insects not included

The keys include virtually all types of damage and wood-boring insect larvae likely to be encountered in buildings. A very few types which occur rarely and which do not require remedial treatment have been excluded. If damage or larvae of such insects are encountered they will lead to an identification which, when referring to the detailed description, will obviously be incorrect. In such rare cases, specialist advice can be sought.

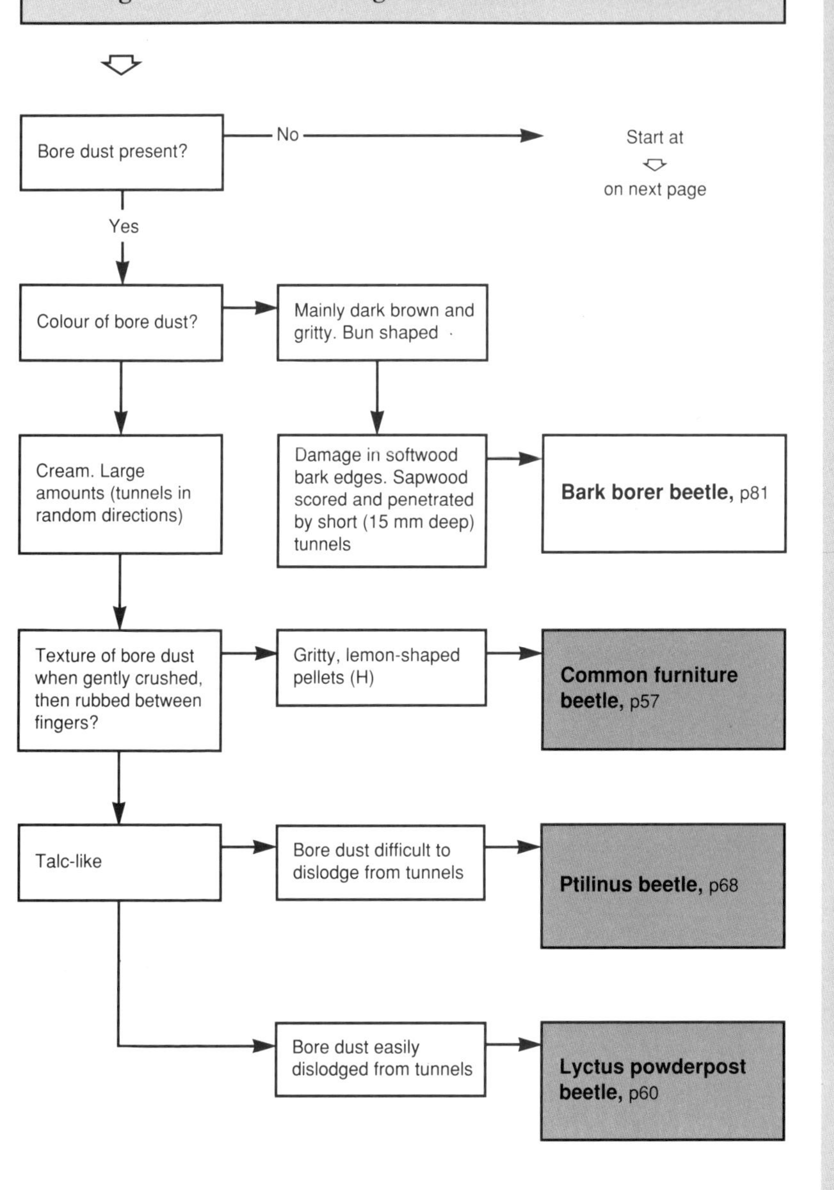
Key for identifying wood-boring insects
Damage with circular emergence holes 1 - 2 mm diameter
Bore dust present?
No
Start at
on next page
Yes
Colour of bore dust?
Mainly dark brown and gritty. Bun shaped
Cream. Large amounts (tunnels in random directions)
Damage in softwood bark edges. Sapwood scored and penetrated by short (15 mm deep) tunnels
Bark borer beetle, p81
Texture of bore dust when gently crushed, then rubbed between fingers?
Gritty, lemon-shaped pellets (H)
Common furniture beetle, p57
Talc-like
Bore dust difficult to dislodge from tunnels
Ptilinus beetle, p68
Bore dust easily dislodged from tunnels
Lyctus powderpost beetle, p60

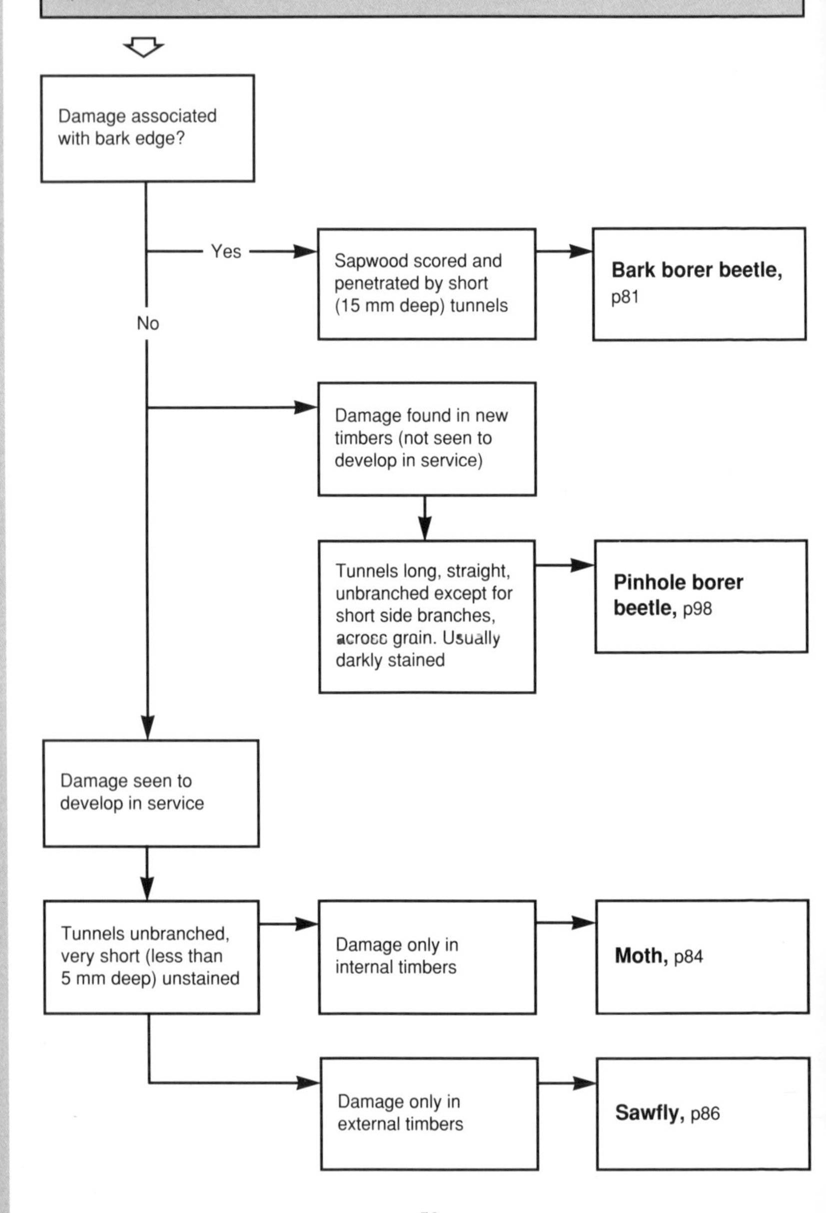
Key for identifying wood-boring insects
Damage with circular emergence holes 1 - 2 mm diameter (continued)
Damage associated with bark edge?
Yes
Sapwood scored and penetrated by short (15 mm deep) tunnels
Bark borer beetle, p81
No
Damage found in new timbers (not seen to develop in service)
Tunnels long, straight, unbranched except for short side branches, across grain. Usually darkly stained
Pinhole borer beetle, p98
Damage seen to develop in service
Tunnels unbranched, very short (less than 5 mm deep) unstained
Damage only in internal timbers
Moth, p84
Damage only in external timbers
Sawfly, p86

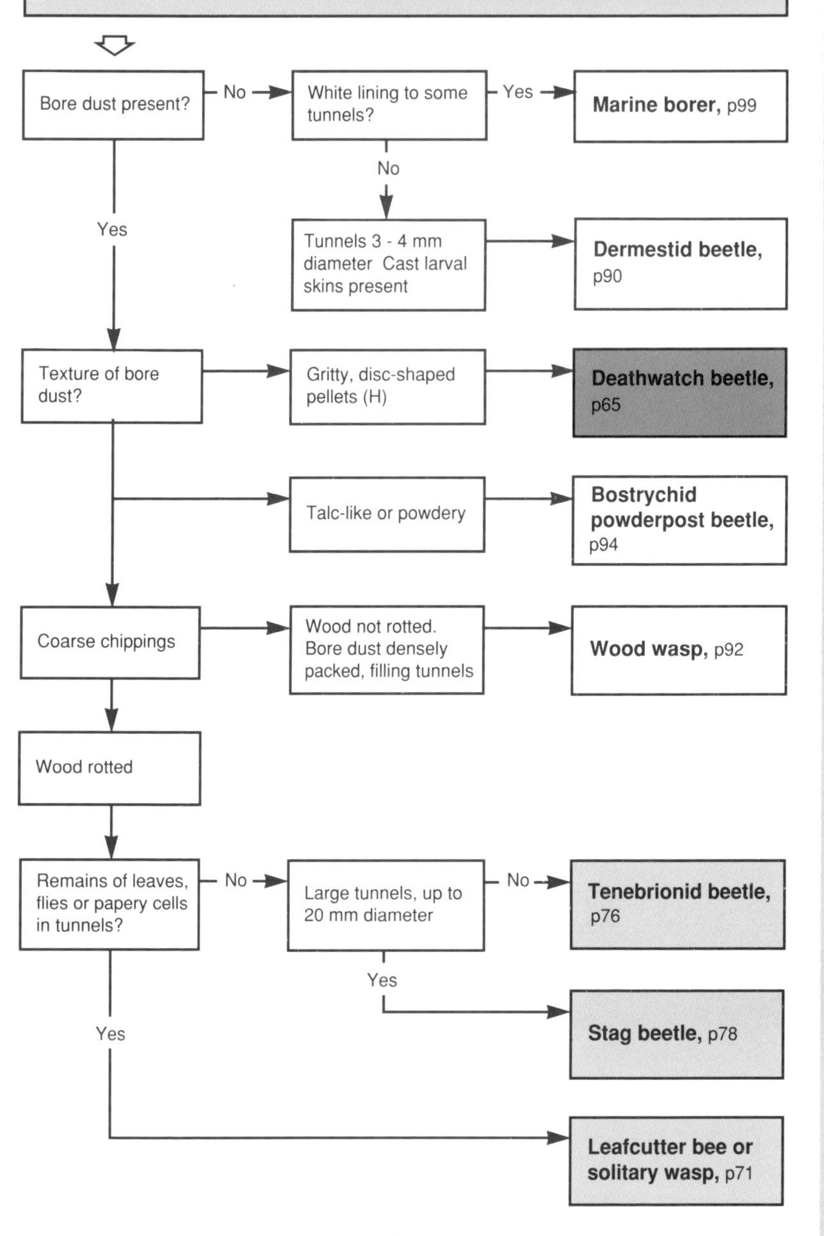
Key for identifying wood-boring insects
Damage with circular emergence holes over 2 mm diameter
Bore dust present?
No
White lining to some tunnels?
Yes
Marine borer, p99
No
Tunnels 3 - 4 mm diameter Cast larval skins present
Dermestid beetle, p90
Yes
Texture of bore dust?
Gritty, disc-shaped pellets (H)
Deathwatch beetle, p65
Talc-like or powdery
Bostrychid powderpost beetle, p94
Coarse chippings
Wood not rotted. Bore dust densely packed, filling tunnels
Wood wasp, p92
Wood rotted
Remains of leaves, flies or papery cells in tunnels?
No
Large tunnels, up to 20 mm diameter
No
Tenebrionid beetle, p76
Yes
Stag beetle, p78
Yes
Leafcutter bee or solitary wasp, p71

Key for identifying wood-boring insects

Damage with oval or irregular emergence holes

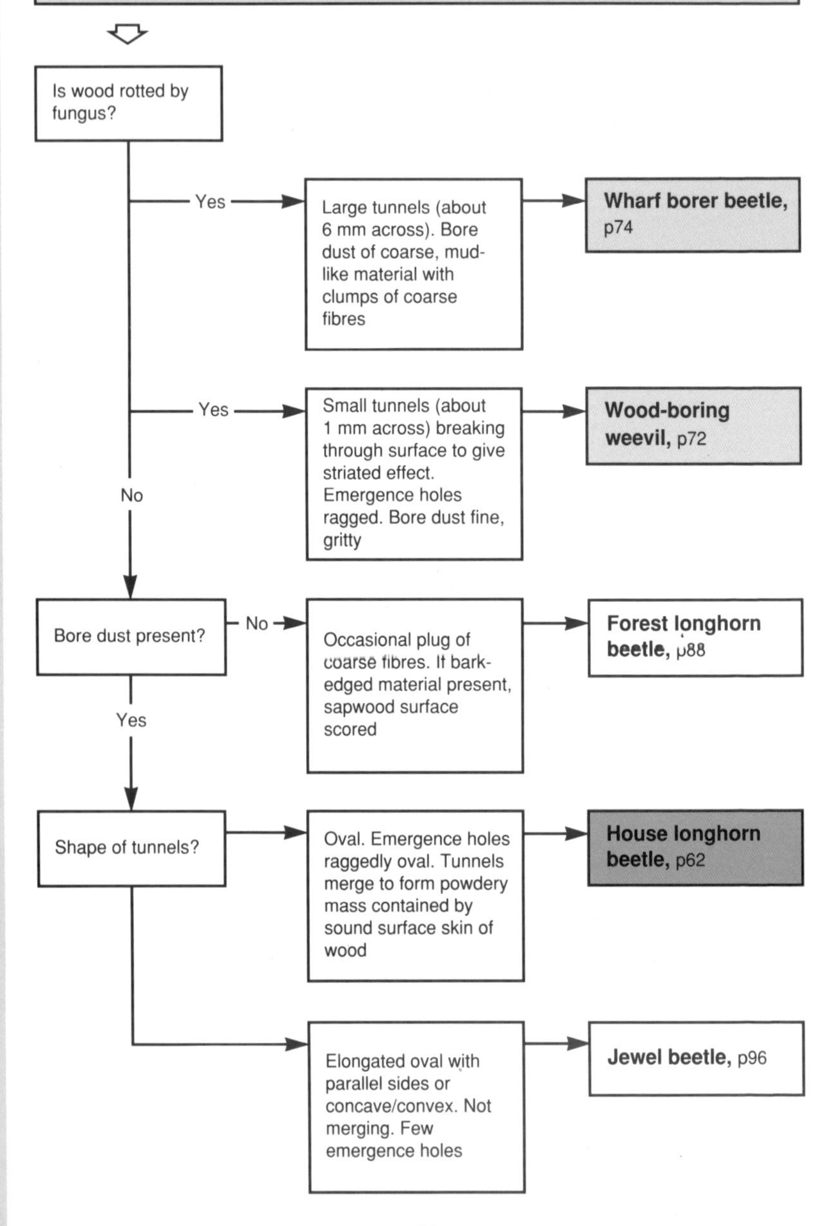

Key for identifying larvae found in building timbers

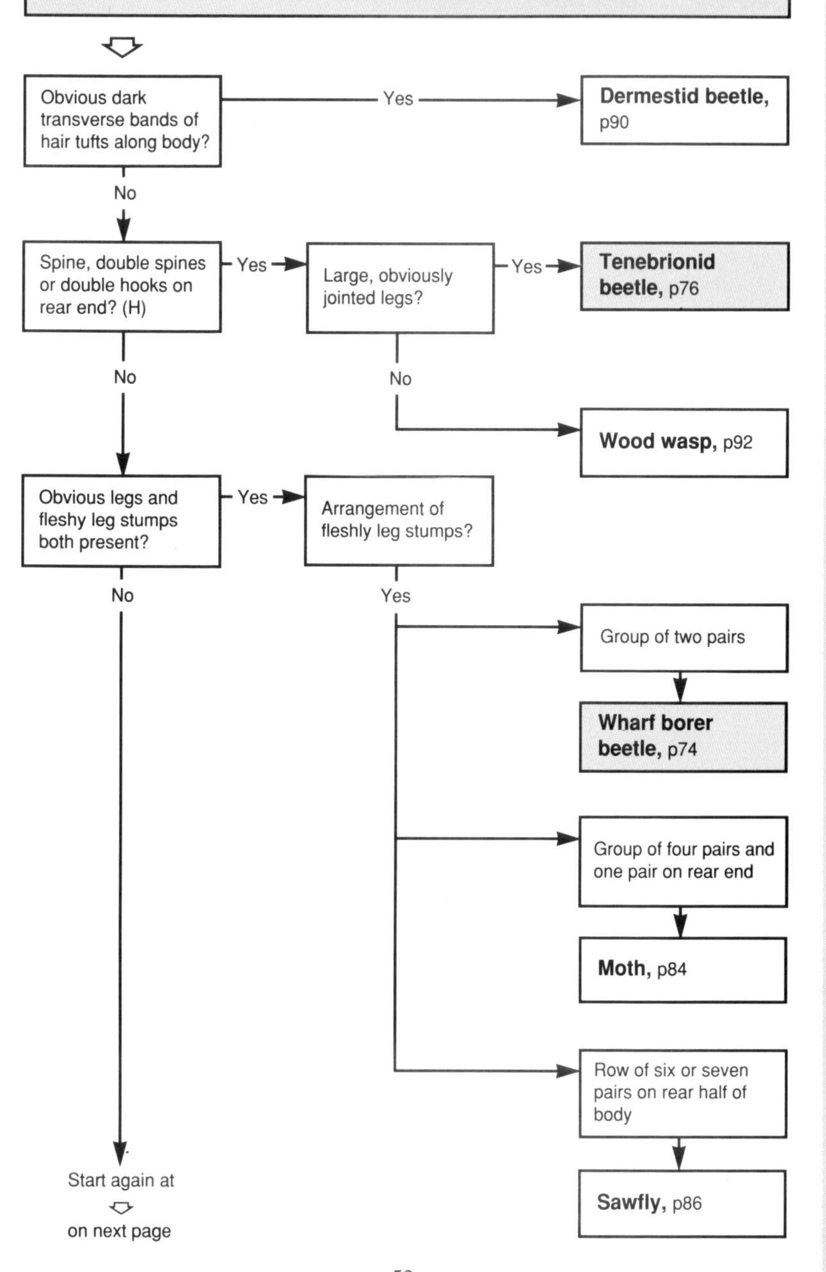

Key for identifying larvae found in building timbers (continued)

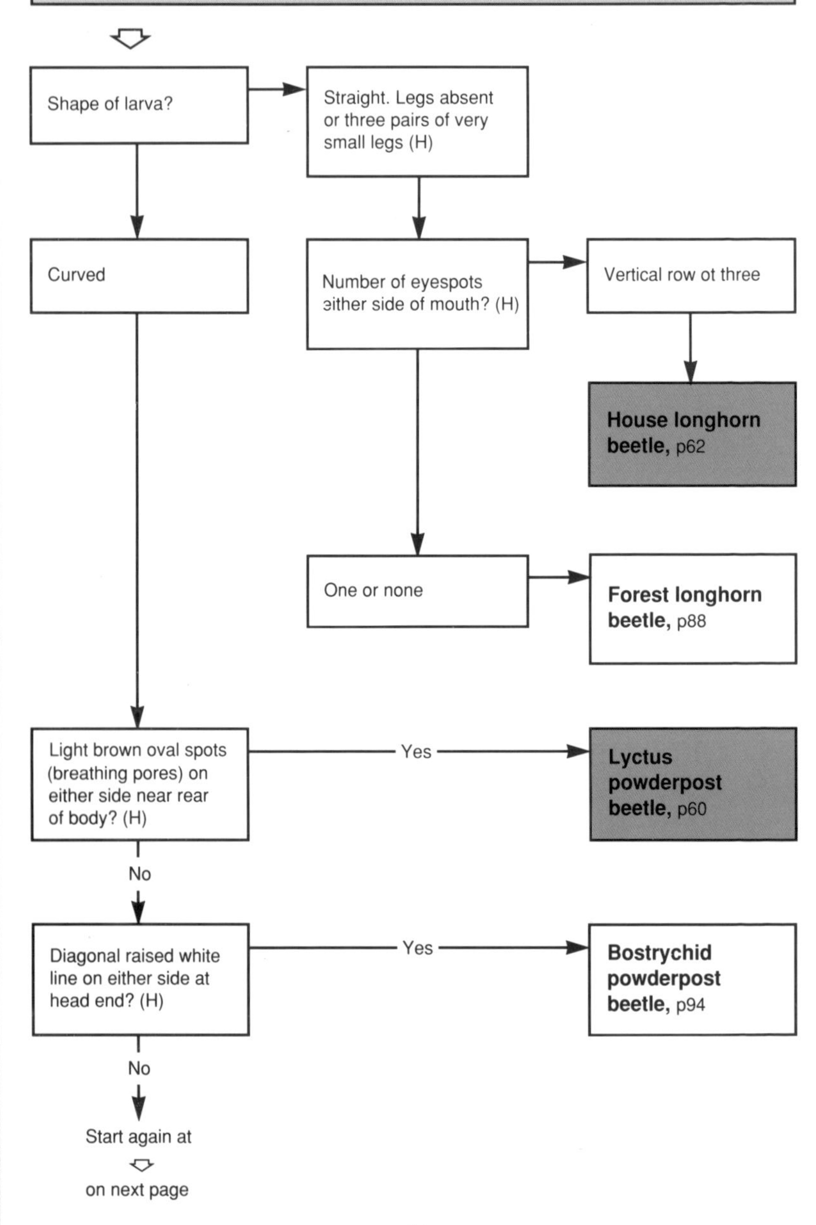

Key for identifying larvae found in building timbers (continued)

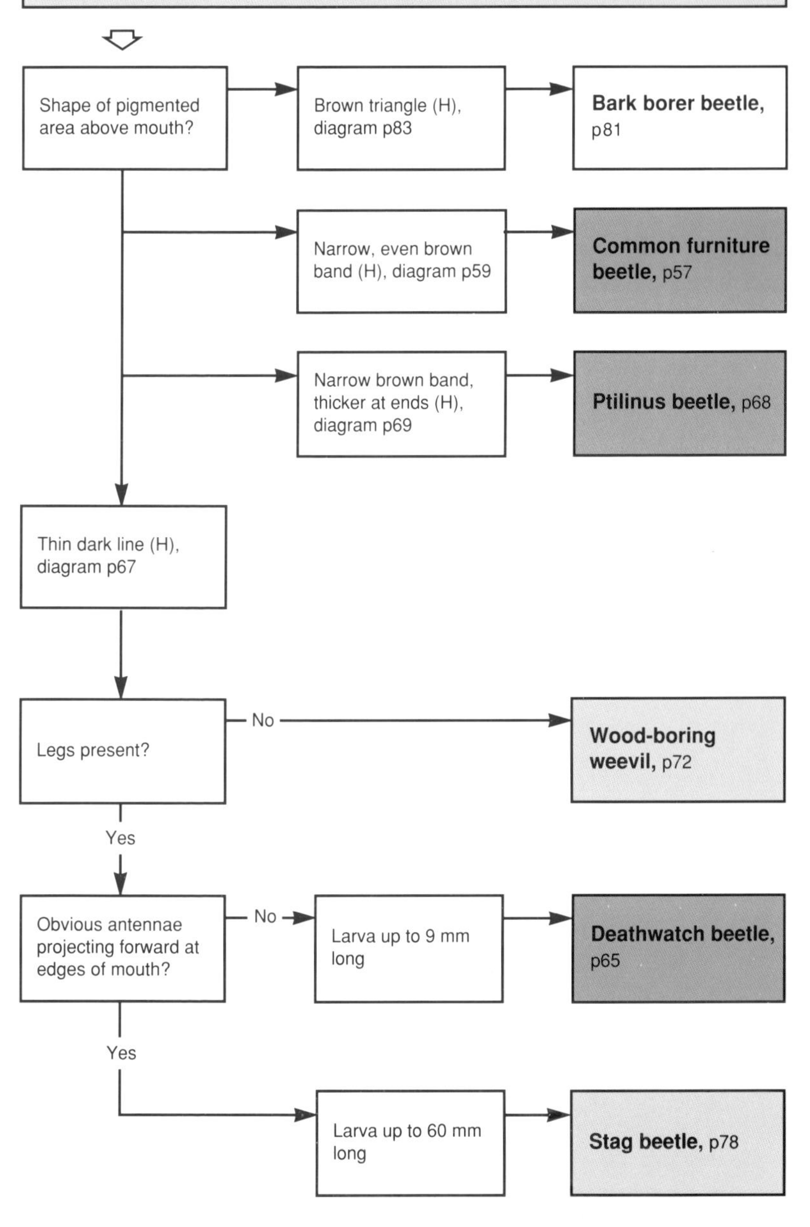

Damage category A insects (insecticidal treatment usually needed)

This part of the book includes the following:

Common furniture beetle

Lyctus powderpost beetle

House longhorn beetle

Deathwatch beetle

Ptilinus beetle

Common furniture beetle

Latin name: *Anobium punctatum*
Other name: woodworm

Habitat:
General Softwoods and European hardwoods.
Solid timber Sapwood only affected, unless wood rot present when it may be found in heartwood also. Very rare in tropical hardwoods. Frequent in older furniture and all constructional timbers, particularly around loft access, timbers in contact with solid walls, under stairs, cupboards and other areas affected by damp.
Panel products Attacks only old birch, beech and oak plywoods with animal based adhesive (blood, fish or casein). Modern plywoods and all other panel products immune, though may be penetrated by emerging adults.

Damage characteristics:
Emergence holes Circular, 1 – 2 mm diameter (old, extinct damage often accompanied by fine pinholes of parasitic wasps).
Tunnels Circular, 1 – 2 mm diameter. Often extensive, random orientation but mainly in the direction of the grain. Often exposed on surface of floorboards by general wear.

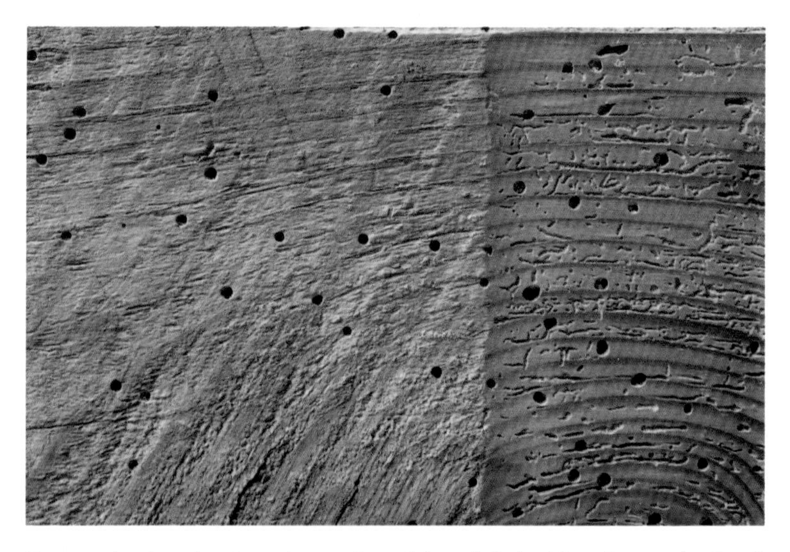

Common furniture beetle — damaged wood (actual size) with surface partly planed to reveal tunnels

Bore dust Cream-coloured, lemon-shaped pellets (H). Gritty when rubbed between fingers.

Likely mis-identifications Bark borer beetle, page 81; pinhole borer beetle, page 98; Ptilinus beetle, page 68; Lyctus powderpost beetle, page 60; deathwatch beetle, page 65; moths, page 84; wood-boring weevils, page 72.

Common furniture beetle — bore dust (× 10)

Remedial treatment[16]**:**
Usual Organic-solvent, emulsion or paste. Damage in very old constructional timbers may often be inactive and, if so, will not require treatment.
Other types Smokes or dichlorvos strips.

Insect characteristics and location:
Adult 3 – 5 mm long, dull brown. Lines of pits on wing covers (H). Often confused with *Stegobium* species (see page 102). Found on and around damaged timber during late March to early August, particularly in warm weather. Attracted to windows and white surfaces.

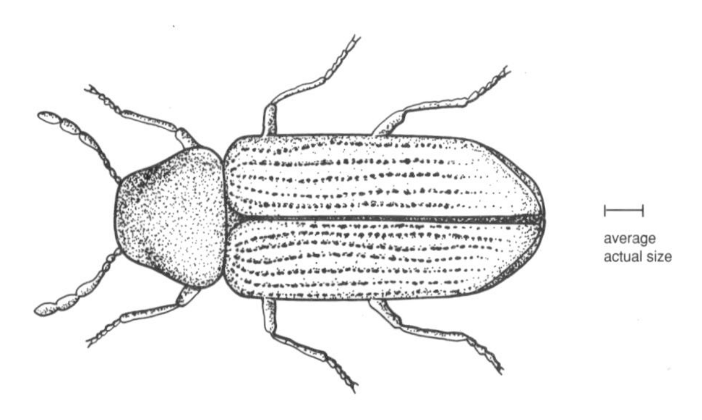

Common furniture beetle — adult (from above)

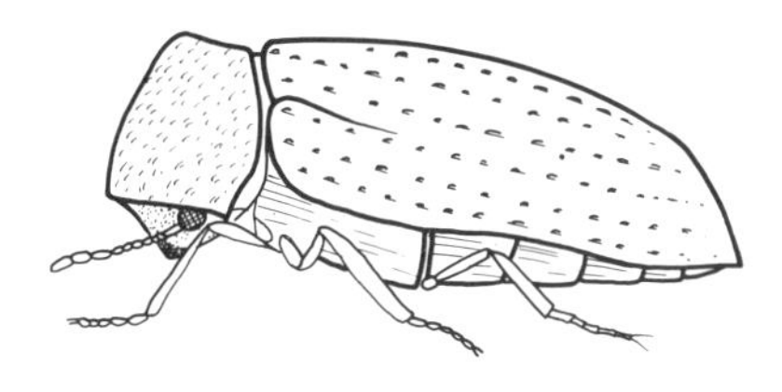

Common furniture beetle — adult (from the side)

Larva Up to 6 mm long, curved, pale cream. Three pairs of legs (H). Narrow dark band over mouth parts (H). Found all year round in infested wood. Often few in number. Absent in extinct infestations.

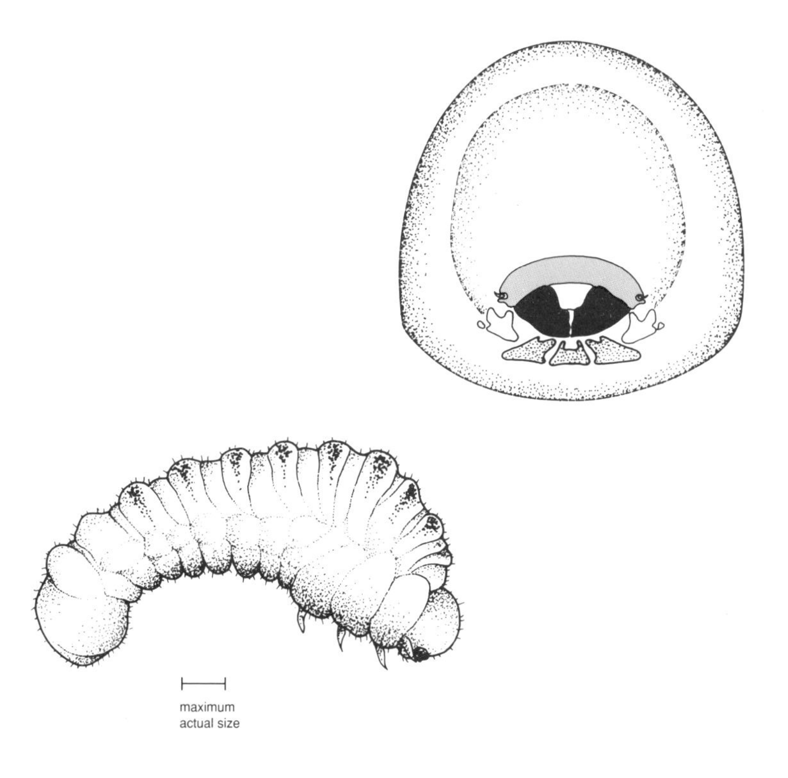

Common furniture beetle — larva (from the side and detail of mouth parts)

Lyctus powderpost beetle

Latin names: *Lyctus brunneus* (and rarely *Lyctus linearis)*

Habitat:
General Sapwood of tropical and European hardwoods, principally oak and elm, with large pores and high starch content. Not found in softwoods.
Solid timber Damage almost always originates in stockyard or storeroom infestation. Only found in timber containing adequate starch and usually with pores large enough for female beetle to lay eggs in. Common in furniture and occasionally in block or strip flooring.
Panel products Veneers, plywood and blockboard are susceptible.

Damage characteristics:
Emergence holes Circular, 1 – 2 mm diameter.
Tunnels Circular, 1 – 2 mm diameter, random orientation but mostly parallel to grain. May be missed in initial stages of attack. In later stages sapwood almost completely disintegrates, leaving thin, intact surface skin of wood.
Bore dust Cream-coloured. Fine, talc-like when rubbed between fingers. May accumulate in small piles beneath emergence holes. Easily shaken out of tunnels.
Likely mis-identifications Common furniture beetle, page 57; Ptilinus beetle, page 68; pinhole borer beetle, page 98; bark borer beetle, page 81; Bostrychid powderpost beetle, page 94.

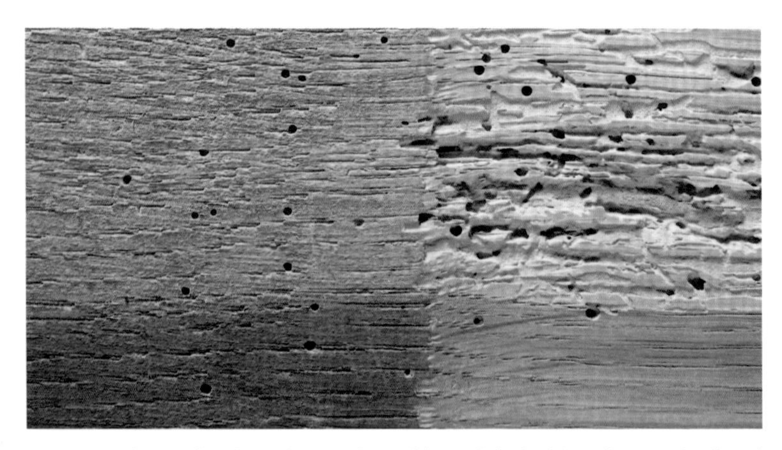

Lyctus powderpost beetle — damaged wood (actual size) with surface partly planed to reveal tunnels

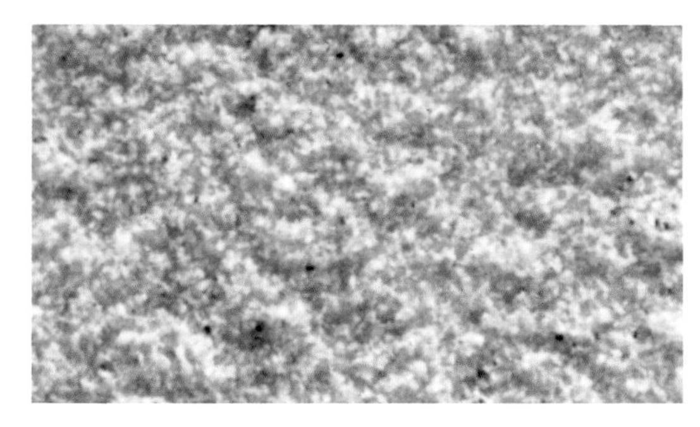

Lyctus powderpost beetle — bore dust (× 10)

Remedial treatment
Organic solvent or paste where sapwood is easily accessible. Treatment to furniture or flooring rarely justified on cost terms and often ineffective because finishes or mastic adhesives prevent uptake. Damage in old timber or furniture will probably be inactive and therefore not require treatment. Regular inspection of stored stock and kiln sterilisation of infested material necessary to prevent further recurrence.

Insect characteristics and location:
Adult 4 – 7 mm long, reddish brown to black. Flattened and elongated with roughly parallel sides compared with rounded shape of common furniture beetle. Found on or around damaged timber, particularly during May to September but throughout year in heated buildings.
Larva Up to 6 mm long, curved, pale cream. Three pairs of small legs (H). Light brown oval spots (breathing pores) on either side at rear of body (H). Found all year round in infested wood.

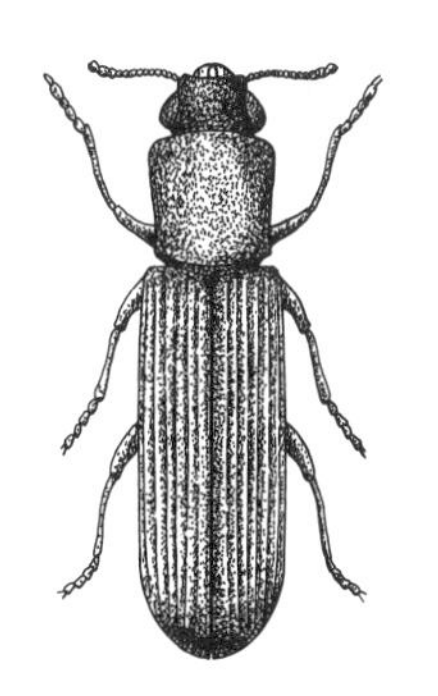

Lyctus powderpost beetle — adult (from above)

average actual size

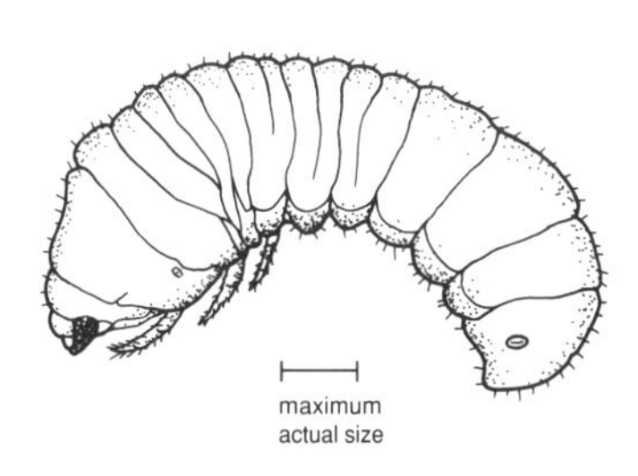

Lyctus powderpost beetle — larva (from the side)

House longhorn beetle

Latin name: *Hylotrupes bajulus*

Habitat:
General Sapwood of most softwoods, particularly roofing timbers.
Solid timber At present common only in area of England SW of London (mainly Surrey) where special Building Regulations exist to protect structural timber and prevent further spread. Small inactive infestations are common in buildings over 100 years old in London. Isolated infestations in other parts of country usually stem from imported infested packing cases.
Panel products Very occasionally found in softwood plywood.

Damage characteristics:
General May be overlooked in early stages. With large infestations, larval feeding may be audible on warm days as scraping noise.
Emergence holes Few, large, oval, often ragged, 6 – 10 mm diameter.
Tunnels Oval, 6 – 10 mm diameter. Extensive and join up to cause almost complete disintegration of sapwood but leaving thin, intact, surface skin. Dust-filled tunnels may cause blisters or corrugations on surface of wood which may be observed with oblique lighting from torch.
Bore dust Cream-coloured, sausage-shaped pellets (H). Gritty when rubbed between fingers. Small chips and wood fibres may be present (H).
Likely mis-identifications Forest longhorn beetle, page 88; jewel beetle, page 96; wharf borer beetle, page 74; wood wasp, page 92; Tenebrionid beetle, page 76; Bostrychid powderpost beetle, page 94.

Remedial treatment Organic solvent or paste. Inspect thoroughly and remove powdered material to determine extent of infestation and any signs of structural weakening. Remove and burn all badly-damaged timber. NOTE: details of suspected outbreaks should be reported to the Building Research Establishment's Timber Division which maintains records of infestations in the UK.

House longhorn beetle — bore dust (× 10)

House longhorn beetle damage (actual size) — emergence holes

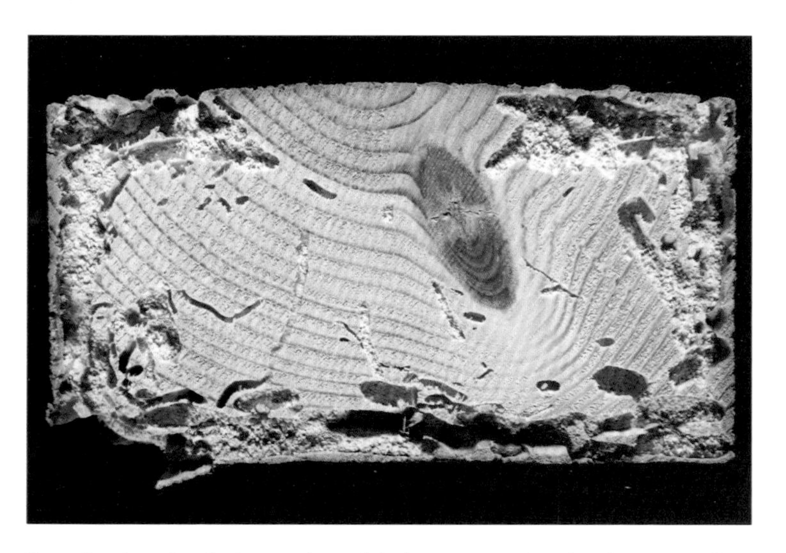

House longhorn beetle damage (actual size) — cross-section showing extent of damage to sapwood and surface skin of sound wood

Insect characteristics and location:

Adult 10 – 12 mm long, black or dull brown. Smooth central line on thorax flanked by two shiny black bumps. Two grey patches of hairs on wing covers. Found on or around infested timber, July to October, particularly on warm days.

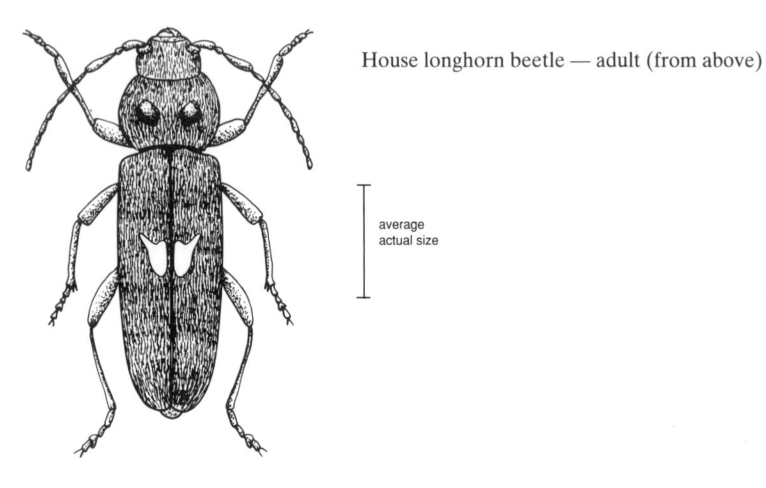

House longhorn beetle — adult (from above)

Larva Up to 30 mm long, straight, pale cream. Three pairs of very small legs (H). Three small black dots arranged in a vertical row on either side of mouth (H). Found all year round in infested wood.

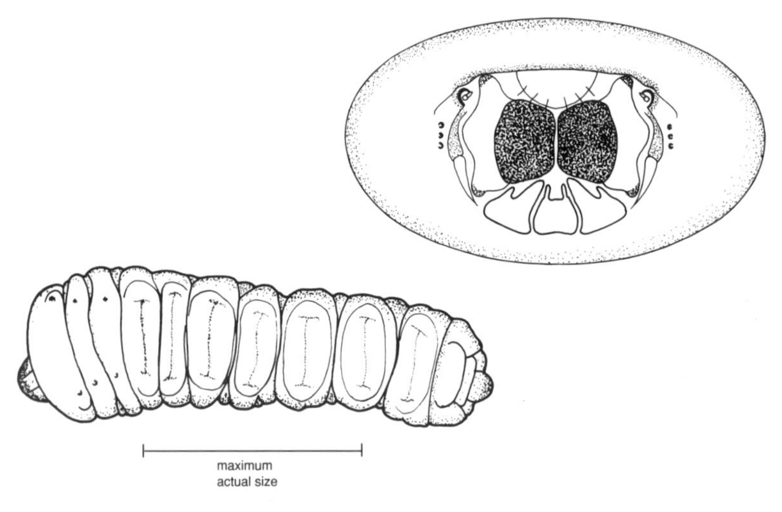

House longhorn beetle — larva (from above and detail of mouth parts)

Deathwatch beetle

Latin name: *Xestobium rufovillosum*

Habitat:
General Sapwood and heartwood of partially decayed hardwoods, chiefly oak.
Solid timber Often found in historic buildings where large quantities of oak or elm used structurally. Softwoods rarely attacked except when in contact with infested hardwood. Dampness essential for establishment and promoting rapid development, although attack can continue, albeit slowly, in drier timber. Found particularly in areas prone to dampness — wall plates, ends of floor joists, lintels and other built-in timbers. Damage often extreme in concealed bearing ends of timbers inserted into damp walls. In conjunction with fungus may hollow out centre of large section beams.

Damage characteristics:
Emergence holes Circular, 3 mm diameter
Tunnels Circular, 3 mm diameter. Often extensive, random orientation, mainly in direction of grain.

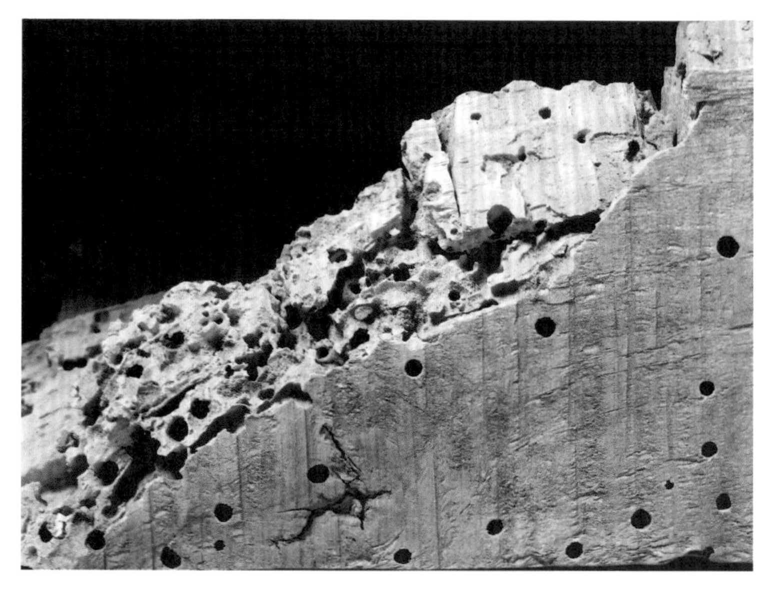

Deathwatch beetle — damaged wood (actual size)

Deathwatch beetle — bore dust (× 10)

Bore dust Cream-coloured, disc-shaped pellets (H). Gritty when rubbed between fingers.
Likely mis-identifications Common furniture beetle, page 57; Bostrychid powderpost beetle, page 94; bark borer beetle, page 81; wood wasp, page 92; Dermestid beetle, page 90; Tenebrionid beetle, page 76; bees or wasps, page 71; marine borer, page 99.

Remedial treatment[15]**:**
Usual Organic solvent or paste. Use pressure injection or gravity feed application to large, well-infested impermeable timbers. Inspect all structural timbers and replace or support any showing structural weakening. Take measures to reduce dampness. NOTE: internal cavities in beams require careful inspection and injection of preservative.
Other types Smokes.

Insect characteristics and location:
Adult 6 – 9 mm long, chocolate brown. Patches of yellow hairs (H). Similar shape to Dermestids but slightly different antennae and thorax (see drawing). Found on or beneath timbers, March to June, particularly in warm weather when they may be heard tapping.

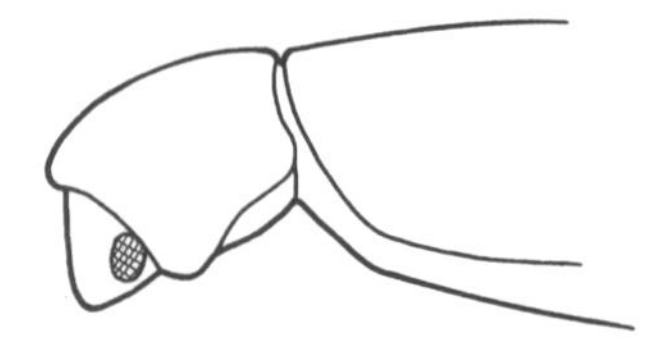

Deathwatch beetle — adult head (left) compared with Dermestid beetle (right)

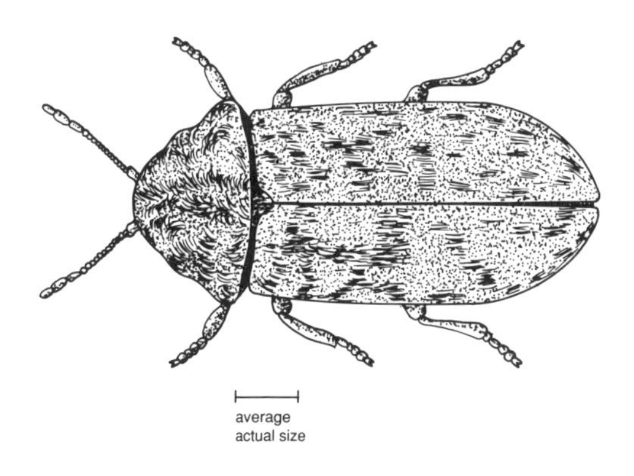

Deathwatch beetle — adult (from above

Larva Up to 9 mm long, curved, pale cream. Three pairs of small legs (H). Covered in fine gold hairs (H). Thin dark line above mouth parts (H). Can be confused with bark borer beetle (see page 81). Found within timber all year round but may be located deep within large size timber. Occasionally fall from severely damaged wood and are found on floor beneath.

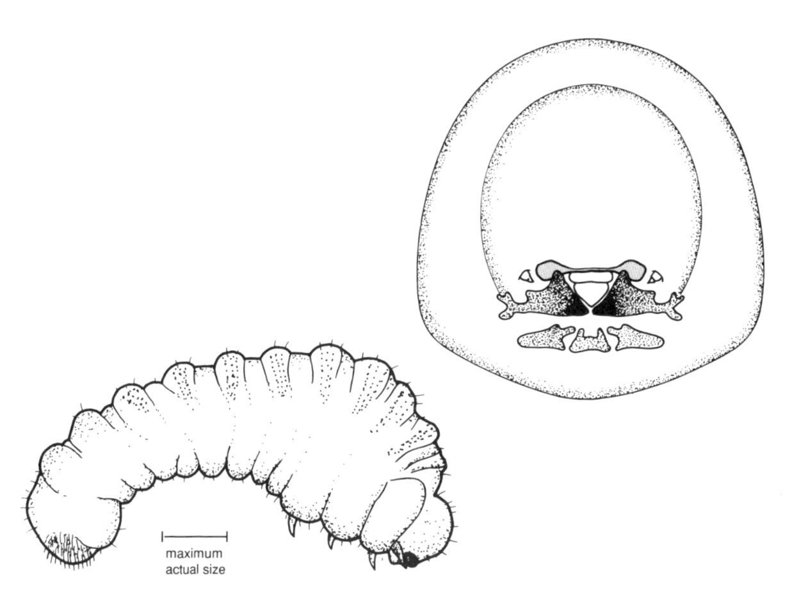

Deathwatch beetle — larva (from the side and detail of mouth parts)

Ptilinus beetle

Latin name: *Ptilinus pectinicornis*

Habitat Limited range of European hardwoods — mainly beech, elm, hornbeam, maple. Damage often originates in stockyards or stockrooms. In buildings, mainly found in furniture.

Damage characteristics:
Emergence holes Circular, 1 – 2 mm diameter.
Tunnels Circular, 1 – 2 mm diameter. Random orientation, mainly in the direction of the grain.
Bore dust Cream coloured. Very densely packed in tunnels and not easily dislodged. Fine, talc-like when crushed and rubbed between fingers.
Likely mis-identifications Lyctus powderpost beetle, page 60; common furniture beetle, page 57; bark borer beetle, page 81; pinhole borer beetle, page 98; sawfly, page 86; moth, page 84.

Remedial treatment Organic solvent, emulsion or paste. (Replacement may be more effective.)

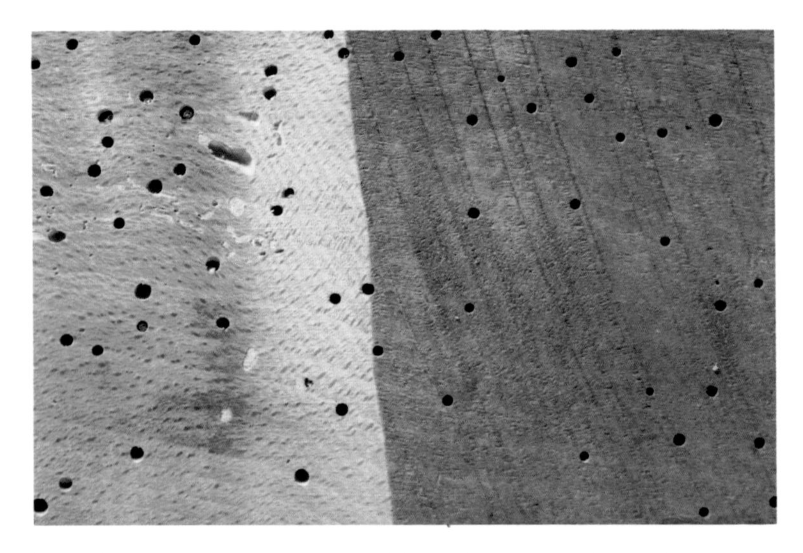

Ptilinus beetle — damaged wood (actual size) with surface partly planed to reveal tunnels

Insect characteristics and location:
Adult 4 – 6 mm long, elongated cylindrical shape. Thorax black or brown. Wing covers reddish brown, pitted (H). Antennae distinctive — male, comb-like; female, saw-like. Found on or around damaged timber, May to July.
Larva Up to 6 mm long, curved, pale cream. Transverse bands of fine hairs (spinules) (H). Three pairs of small legs (H). Narrow brown band over mouth parts (thicker at ends) (H). Found all year round in infested wood.

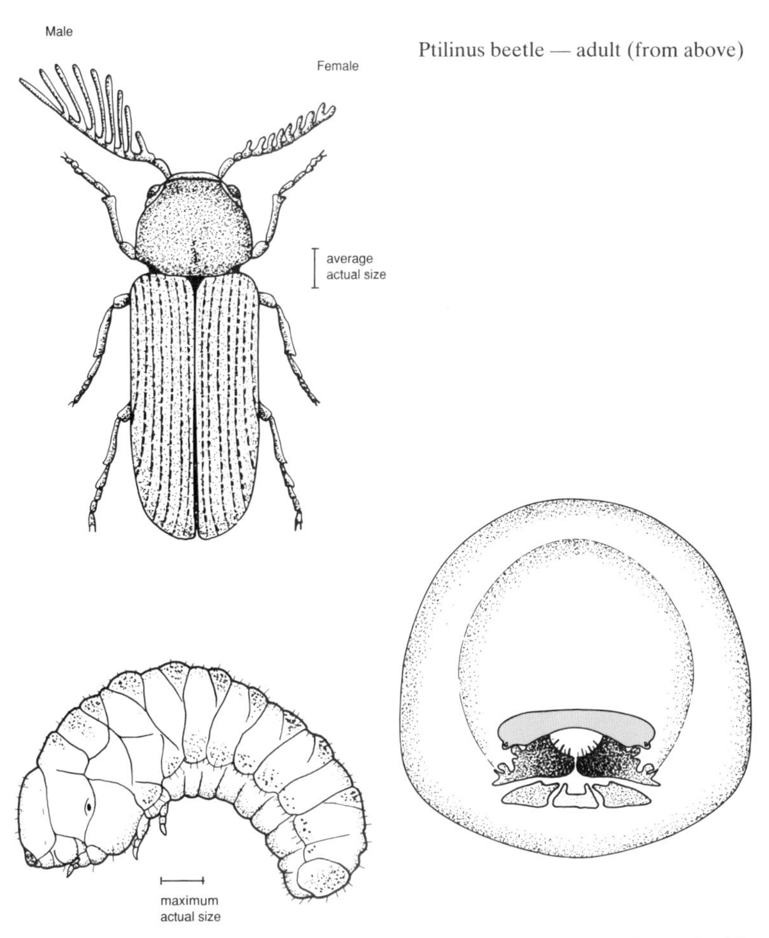

Ptilinus beetle — adult (from above)

Ptilinus beetle — larva (from the side and detail of mouth parts)

Damage category B insects (treatment necessary only to control associated wood rot)

This part of the book includes the following:

Leafcutter bees and solitary wasps

Wood-boring weevils

Wharf borer beetle

Tenebrionid beetles

Stag beetles

Leafcutter bees and solitary wasps

Latin names: *Megachile* spp (bees) and *Crabro* spp (wasps)

Habitat Decayed wood, normally outdoors (eg, in dead trees and fence posts), but may infest badly decayed exterior building timbers such as window joinery, fascias, cladding, exposed ends of rafters and even wall plates. Some bee species may bore into soft mortar or stone and cause serious weakening over a number of years.

Damage characteristics:
General Produce large, circular emergence holes and tunnels (6 – 7 mm diameter), partially plugged with coarse chippings. Tunnels may contain dead leaves formed into cells (bees) or membraneous cells and many small metallic-coloured fragmented remains and wings of dead flies (wasps).
Likely mis-identifications Wood wasp, page 92; deathwatch beetle, page 65; Tenebrionid beetles, page 76.

Remedial treatment No insecticidal treatment required. Remove source of dampness and dry out sound timber; replace decayed timber (see page 35). Re-point damaged mortar with harder cement-lime-sand mix.

Insect characteristics:
Adult Appearance variable, but all have general wasp or bee characteristics.
Larva Both types have legless non-mobile larvae reared in cells in tunnels. Present during spring.

Bee or wasp — damaged wood (actual size)

Wood-boring weevils

Latin names: *Pentarthrum huttoni* and *Euophryum confine*

Habitat Decayed softwoods and hardwoods in damp conditions — poorly ventilated ground floors, cellars, and wood in contact with damp solid floors or walls are particularly susceptible. Damage secondary to fungal decay. Also attacks plywood in these conditions.

Damage characteristics:
Emergence holes Small, ragged, about 1 mm diameter.
Tunnels Numerous, normally in the direction of the grain. Often break through to wood surface.
Bore dust Fine, gritty.
Likely mis-identifications Common furniture beetle, page 57.

Remedial treatment No insecticidal treatment required. Remove source of dampness and dry out sound timber. Replace decayed timber (see page 35). Infestation of sound dry wood not possible.

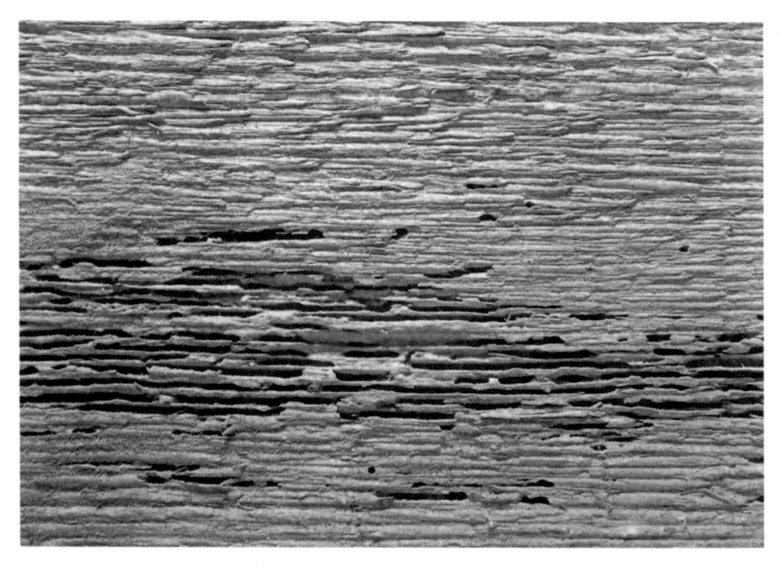

Wood-boring weevil — damaged wood (actual size)

Insect characteristics and location:

Adult 3 – 5 mm long, brownish-black. Distinctive long snout (H). Antennae one-third distance along snout (H). Found on or around infested wood all year round. May migrate in large numbers into rooms adjacent to damage, particularly during summer months or if drying takes place.

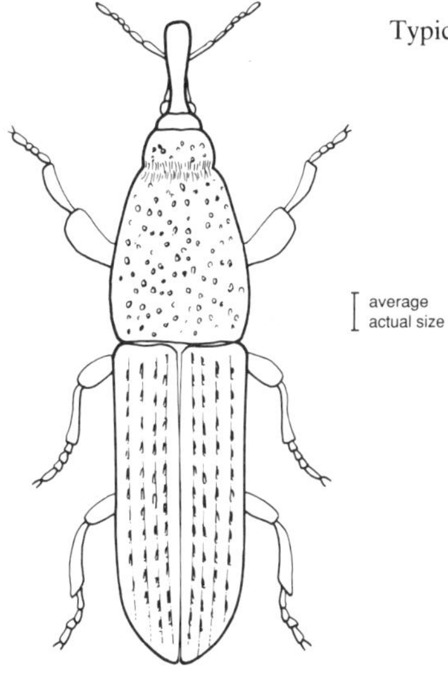

Typical wood-boring weevil — adult (from above)

Larva Up to 4 mm long, curved, pale cream. No legs (H). Thin dark line above mouth parts (H). Found in infested wood all year round.

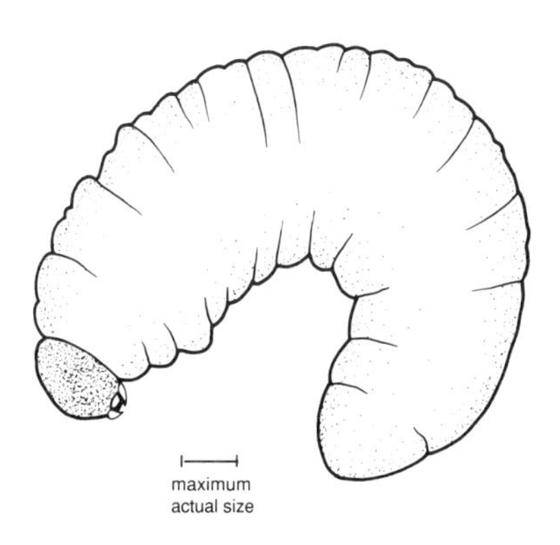

Typical wood-boring weevil — larva (from the side)

Wharf borer beetle

Latin name: *Nacerdes melanura*

Habitat Very damp, decayed softwoods and hardwoods. Often found in wharf timbers and other timber in freshwater or brackish conditions. In buildings, often in cellars, or in timber which has become buried. Sometimes found in older wooden boats.

Damage characteristics:
General Large, oval emergence holes, about 6 mm across, leading to irregular galleries packed with hardened, mud-like material and plugs of coarse fibres.
Likely mis-identifications House longhorn beetle, page 62; forest longhorn beetle, page 88.

Remedial treatment No insecticidal treatment required. Remove source of dampness and dry out sound timber. Replace decayed timber (see page 35). Reinfestation of sound wood not possible.

Wharf borer beetle — damaged wood (actual size)

Insect characteristics and location:

Adult 6 – 12 mm long, elongated. Pale reddish brown with distinctive black tip to wing covers. Long antennae. Similar to forest longhorn beetle (see page 88) but without kidney shaped eye (H) and with antennae attached to head well before eye (H). Found on or around damaged timber in summer. Known to invade nearby buildings in large numbers causing nuisance.

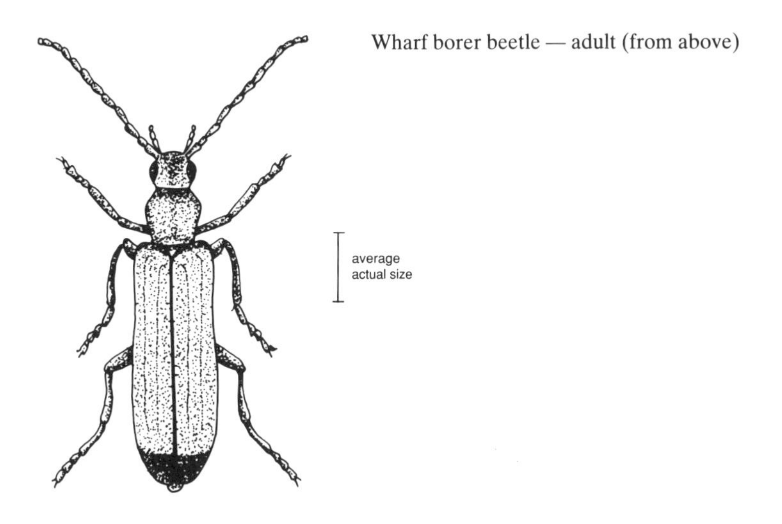

Wharf borer beetle — adult (from above)

Larva Up to 30 mm long, slender, greyish white. Three pairs of large conspicuous legs. Two pairs of fleshy stumps on rear half of body. Fairly mobile. Found on or in damaged timber all year round.

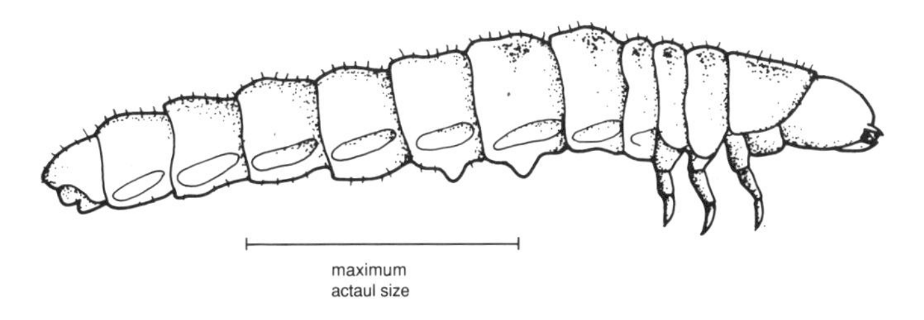

Wharf borer beetle — larva (from the side)

Tenebrionid beetles

Latin names: *Tenebrio mollitor* and other species
Other name: mealworm beetle (*T. mollitor* only)

Habitat Principally flour and flour-based products, but very well rotted timbers also attacked. *Tenebrio mollitor* may also damage sound timbers associated with infested flour.

Damage characteristics:
Tunnels Irregular oval or circular tunnels up to 10 mm diameter, partially filled with coarse, fibrous powder.
Likely mis-identifications House longhorn beetle, page 62; wood wasp, page 92; forest longhorn beetle, page 88; deathwatch beetle, page 65; bees or wasps, page 71.

Remedial treatment No insecticidal treatment necessary. Remove source of dampness and dry out sound timber. Replace decayed timber (see page 35). Unless associated with infested flour, sound wood not attacked.

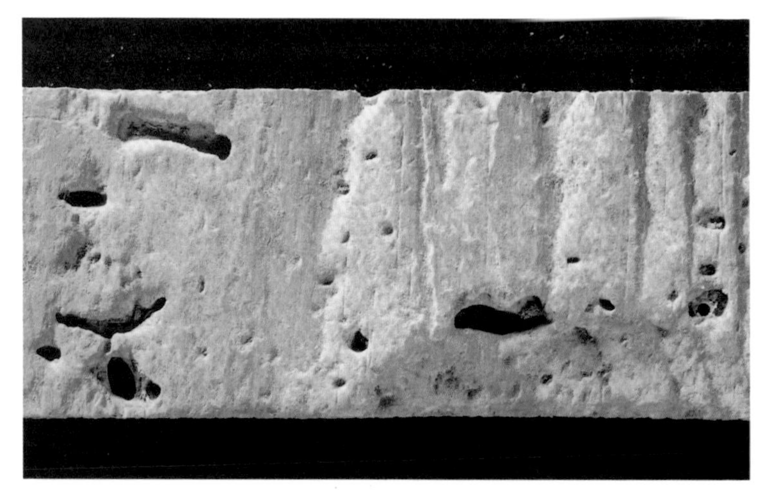

Tenebrionid beetle — damaged wood (actual size)

Insect characteristics and location:

Adult See page 103. Migrates away from damage caused by larvae to other parts of building. Also commonly enters buildings as casual intruder.

Larva Up to 30 mm long, straight, pale yellow. Three pairs of large obviously jointed legs. Pair of small spines at rear end (H) or obvious double hooks (H).

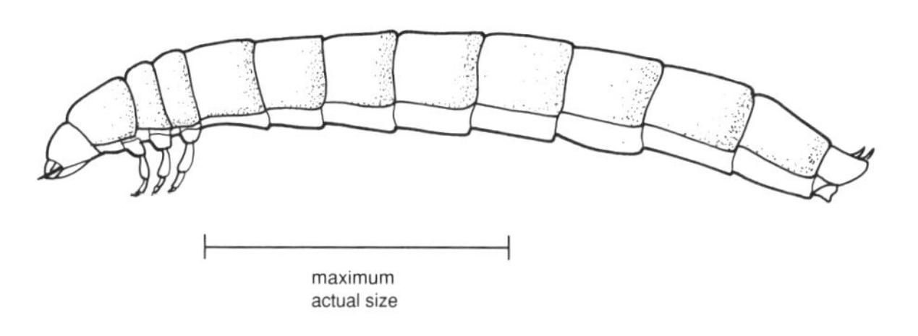

Typical Tenebrionid beetle — larva (from the side)

Stag beetles

Latin names: *Lucanus cervus* and other species of family Lucanidae

Habitat Very well rotted damp timbers, usually hardwoods such as oak and elm, often in contact with damp masonry.

Damage characteristics:
Tunnels Very large irregular tunnels up to 20 mm diameter, and cavities partially filled with coarse fibrous powder.
Likely mis-identifications None, due to size of tunnels.

Stag beetle — damaged wood (shown half actual size)

Remedial treatment No insecticidal treatment required. Remove source of dampness and dry out timber. Replace decayed timber (see page 35). Infestation of sound wood not possible.

Insect characteristics and location:
Adult Rarely found in association with damage.
Larva Very large (up to 60 mm), curved, pale cream. Three pairs of jointed legs. Thin dark line above mouth. Obvious antennae projecting forward at edges of mouth.

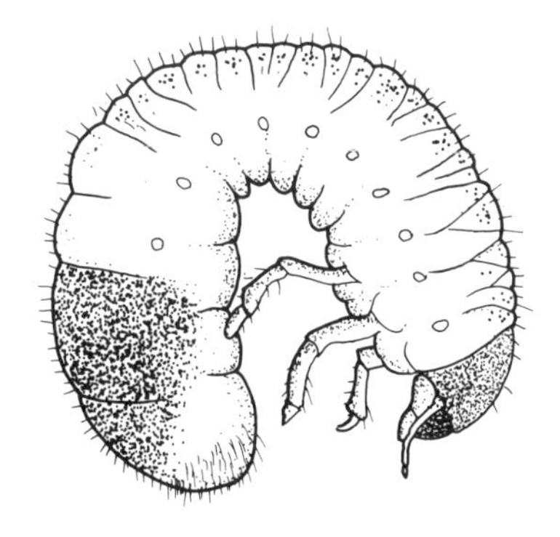

Typical stag beetle — larva (from the side, about actual size)

Damage category C insects (no treatment needed)

This part of the book includes the following:

Bark borer beetle

Moths

Sawfly

Forest longhorn beetles

Dermestid beetles

Wood wasps

Bostrychid powderpost beetles

Jewel beetles

Pinhole borer beetles

Marine borers

Bark borer beetle

Latin name: *Ernobius mollis*
Other name: waney edge borer

Habitat A bark borer of softwoods, usually found outdoors in recently dead trees, incompletely debarked logs, slabs and posts. May be found in dry timber in buildings if bark present.

Damage characteristics:
Emergence holes Circular, 1 – 2 mm diameter, in bark.
Tunnels Short (less than 15 mm deep), empty, mainly in bark but also scoring and penetrating sapwood.
Bore dust Not always present. Bun shaped pellets (H). Gritty when rubbed between fingers. Mainly dark with some cream pellets resulting from feeding in sapwood.
Likely mis-identifications Common furniture beetle, page 57; pinhole borer beetle, page 98; deathwatch beetle, page 65; Lyctus powderpost beetle, page 60; Ptilinus beetle, page 68.

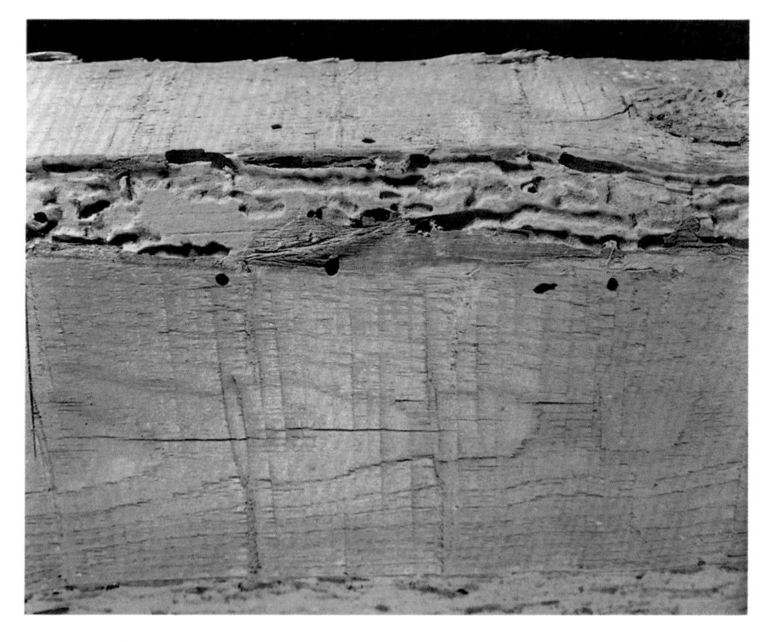

Bark borer beetle — damaged wood (actual size)

Bark borer beetle — bore dust (× 10)

Remedial treatment
None necessary apart from removal of bark.

Insect characteristics and location:
Adult 4 – 6 mm long, shiny reddish brown. Head partly visible from above (H). Long antennae (H). Prominent hairs covering body (H). No pits in wing covers. Found on and around damaged timber, May to August.

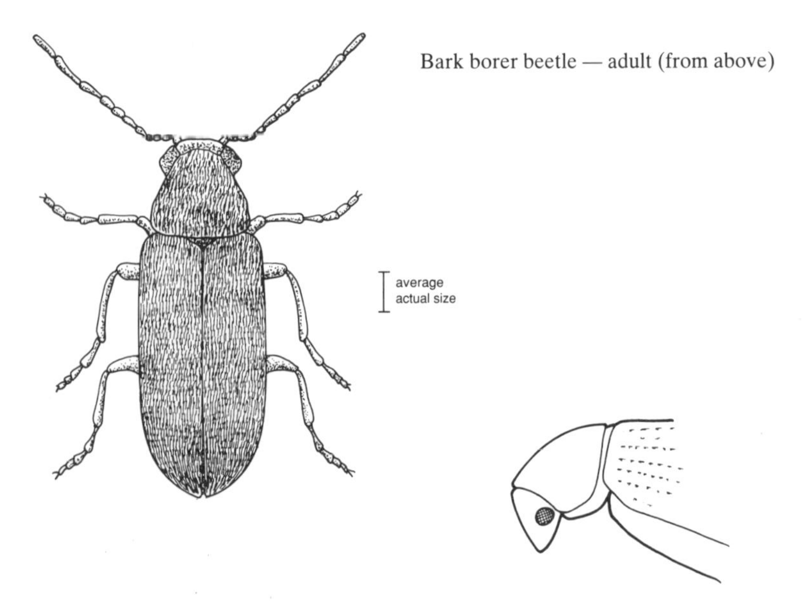

Bark borer beetle — adult (from above)

Bark borer beetle — adult head (from the side)

Larva Up to 6 mm long, curved, pale cream. Three pairs of small legs (H). Brown triangular pigmented area above mouth. Resembles common furniture beetle but is more hairy. Found all year round in infested wood.

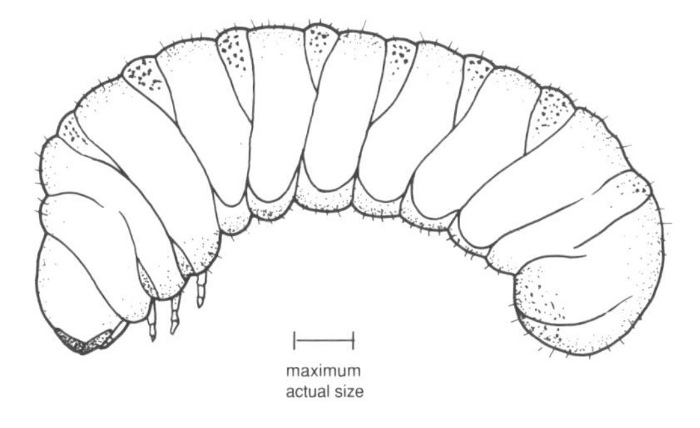

Bark borer beetle — larva (from the side)

Bark borer beetle — larva (detail of mouth parts)

Moths

Latin names: *Tineola bisselliella* (clothes moth), *Hofmannophila pseudospretella* (house moth) and other species

Habitat Fabrics, wool (particularly when soiled with organic matter), seeds, thatch and dry stored food products. May cause superficial scoring of wood in contact with infested material.

Damage characteristics:
General Where infested material is in contact with wood, short (less than 5 mm deep), circular, blind-ended tunnels, 1 – 2 mm diameter, may be found. Severe infestations usually indicate damp conditions.
Likely mis-identifications Common furniture beetle, page 57; Lyctus powderpost beetle, page 60; Ptilinus beetle, page 68; pinhole borer beetle, page 98; bark borer beetle, page 81.

Remedial treatment Sterilise or dispose of infested items. Thoroughly clean affected area to remove larvae. Restore dry conditions.

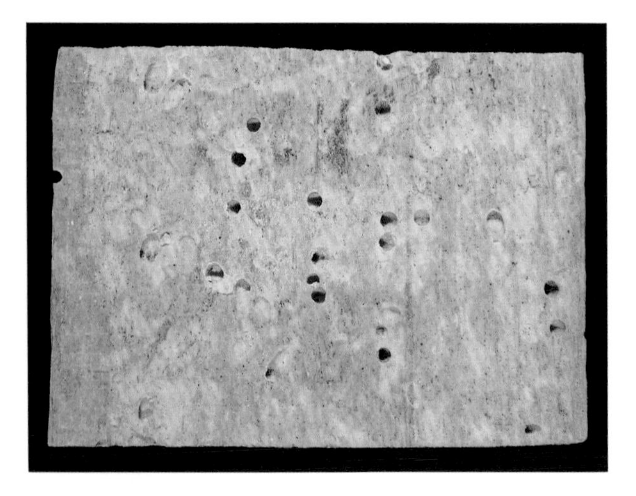

Moth — damaged wood (actual size)

Larval characteristics and location Up to 10 mm long, straight. Pale cream with brownish head. Three pairs of conspicuous legs (H). Four pairs of fleshy stumps on rear half of body, each bearing terminal ring of hooks (H). Found in cracks and crevices in wood, particularly near infested upholstery, carpets and furnishings.

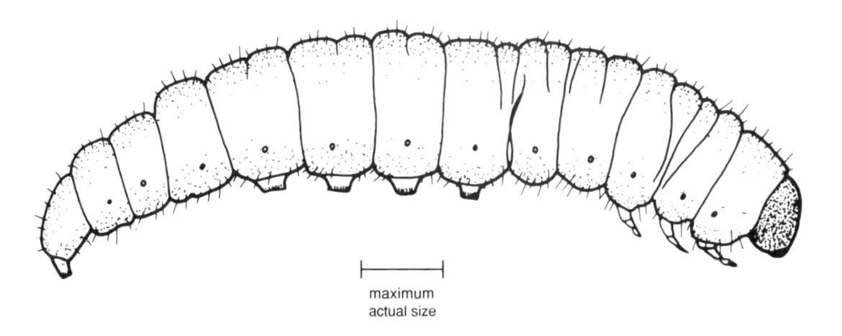

Typical moth — larva (from the side)

Sawfly

Latin name: *Ametastegia glabrata*

Habitat:
General Usually in softwoods
Solid timber Sapwood and heartwood of external timbers, particularly cladding and fencing. May occur in preservative treated wood and durable timbers such as western red cedar. Damage frequently occurs on new sites where various weeds are present which are food for the larvae.
Panel products No recorded cases of damage, but could occur.

Damage characteristics:
Emergence holes/tunnels Very short (usually less than 10 mm) unbranched, circular, 1 – 2 mm diameter. Usually at right angles to horizontal surfaces but may also enter end grain where tunnels may be slightly longer (less than 30 mm).

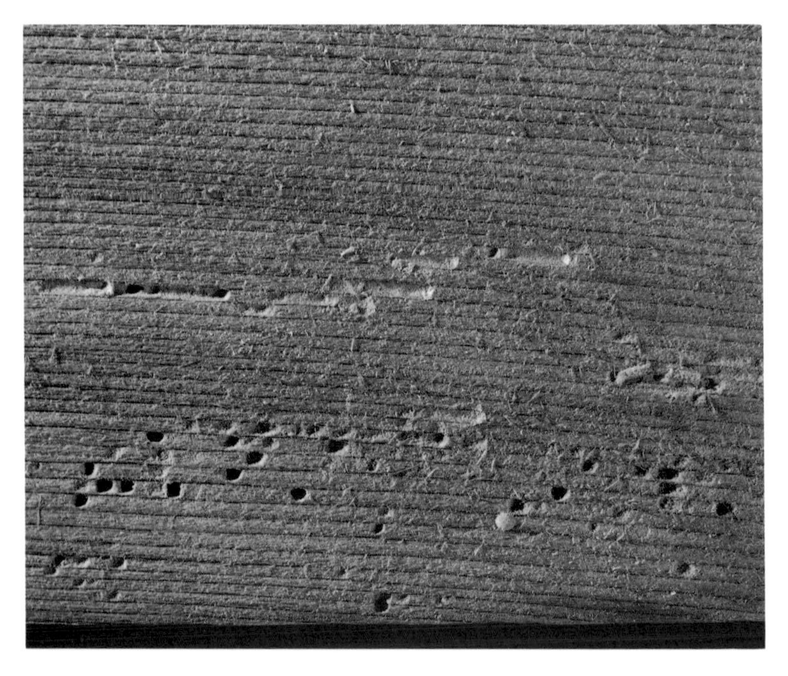

Sawfly — damaged wood (actual size)

Bore dust None.
Likely mis-identifications Pinhole borer beetle, page 98; bark borer beetle, page 81; Ptilinus beetle, page 68; Lyctus powderpost beetle, page 60; common furniture beetle, page 57.

Remedial treatment Remove food plants of larvae (often docks, *Rumex* spp, etc) from immediate area of any affected timber. Spray vegetation and soil at base of badly affected cladding with a general purpose garden insecticide.

Insect characteristics and location:
Adult A winged, fly-like insect, not often seen.
Larva Up to 10 mm long, curved, pale brown or (more often) green. Three pairs of legs; six or seven pairs of fleshy stumps on rear half of body. Found early summer to autumn on food plants, and on and around infected wood.

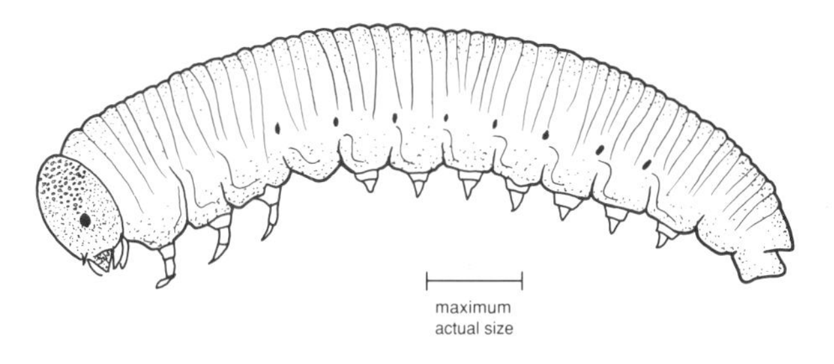

Sawfly — larva (from the side)

Forest longhorn beetles

Latin name: family Cerambycidae — many species

Habitat Imported and British-grown softwoods and hardwoods. Attacks standing and felled trees, and partly dried timber where bark attached. Damaged timber may be incorporated into buildings. Some larvae may survive and emerge later as adults but cannot reinfest dry timber without bark.

Damage characteristics:
Emergence holes Large, oval. Typically 6 – 10 mm across widest dimension.
Tunnels Oval, 6 – 10 mm diameter, in bark and also scoring sapwood. Some deep tunnels at right angles to grain penetrating into sapwood. These may be sectioned during sawing and mistaken for emergence holes.
Bore dust Not present. Tunnels may be plugged with small masses of coarse fibres.
Likely mis-identifications House longhorn beetle, page 62; wood wasp, page 92; wharf borer beetle, page 74; Tenebrionid beetle, page76; jewel beetle, page 96.

Remedial treatment None necessary apart from removal of bark.

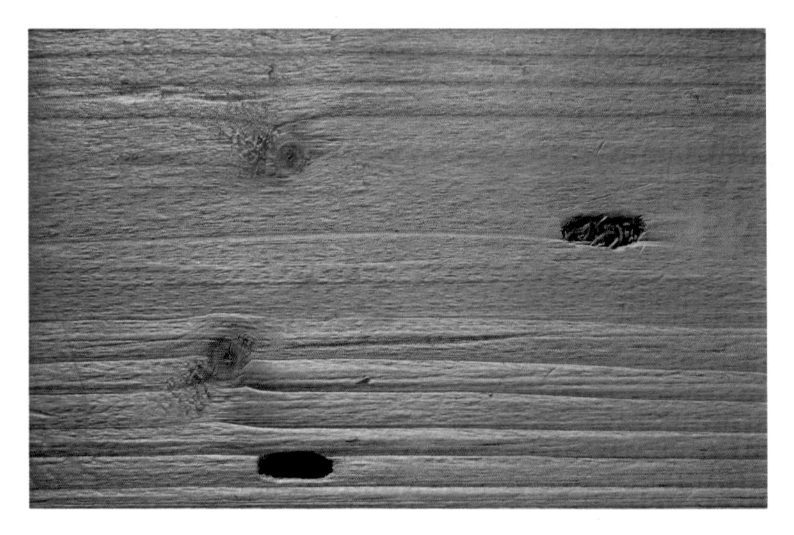

Forest longhorn beetle — damaged wood (actual size)

Insect characteristics and location:

Adult Wide ranging in appearance and size, but common species brown or black with distinctive long antennae arising from the notches of the kidney-shaped eyes (H). Occasionally found on or around wood in spring or emerging from recently dried timber.

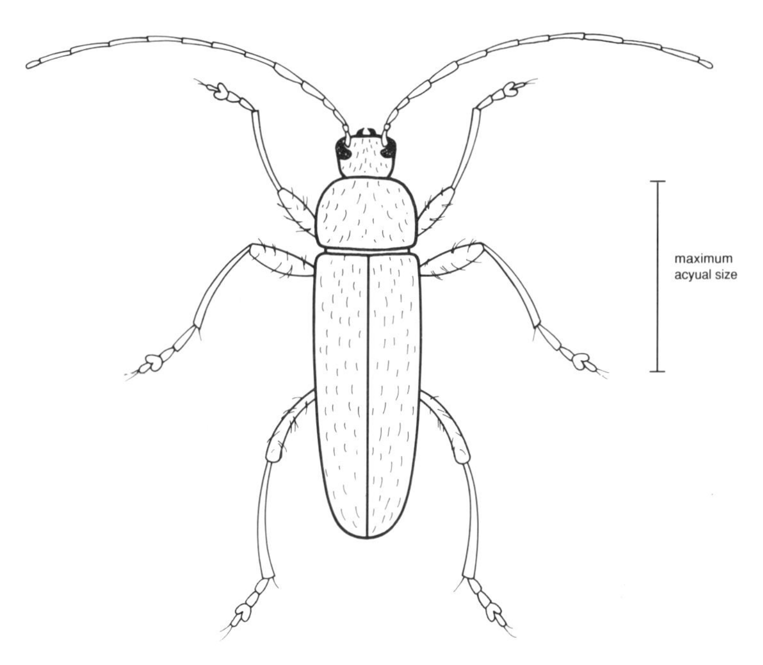

Typical forest longhorn beetle — adult (from above)

Larva Straight, white, long, markedly segmented. Head sunk in thorax. Jaws dark brown. Possibly a single dark eye spot either side of mouth (H). Legs absent or else three minute pairs (H). Found beneath bark and in tunnels in recently felled or converted timber. Occasionally found in recently dried timber.

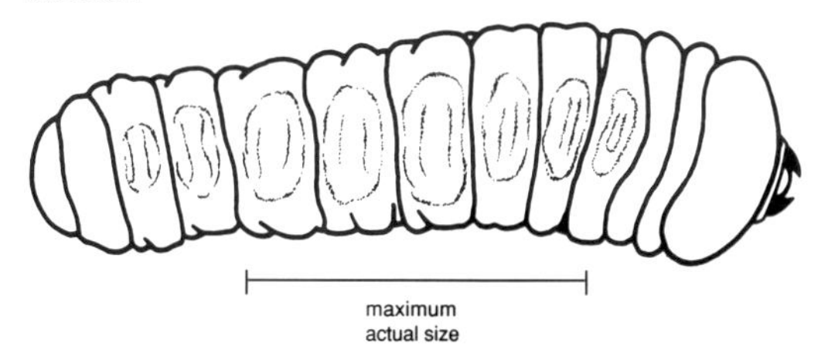

Typical forest longhorn beetle — larva (from above)

Dermestid beetles

Latin name: *Dermestes* spp
Other names: larder beetle, bacon beetle and hide beetle

Habitat Almost any dry material of animal origin (eg, leather, fur, feathers, dead mice and meat). Not primary wood feeders, but fully grown larvae frequently bore short refuge tunnels into timber adjacent to food source. Heavy infestations in food storage rooms and chicken houses may cause serious damage. Small infestations may be found adjacent to birds nests in domestic roofs.

Damage characteristics:
General Circular entry holes, 3 – 4 mm diameter, leading to short blind-ending tunnels, usually free from bore dust and sometimes up to 10 mm long. Cast larval skins often found in tunnels.
Likely mis-identifications Deathwatch beetle, page 65.

Remedial treatment Locate and remove food source. Apply insecticidal spray or dust to heavy infestations.

Dermestid beetle — damaged wood (actual size)

Insect characteristics and location:
Adult 4 – 7 mm long, black or brown, with or without white hairs, depending on species. Similar shape to deathwatch beetle but slightly different antennae and thorax (see page 66). Found adjacent to food source but may disperse some distance.

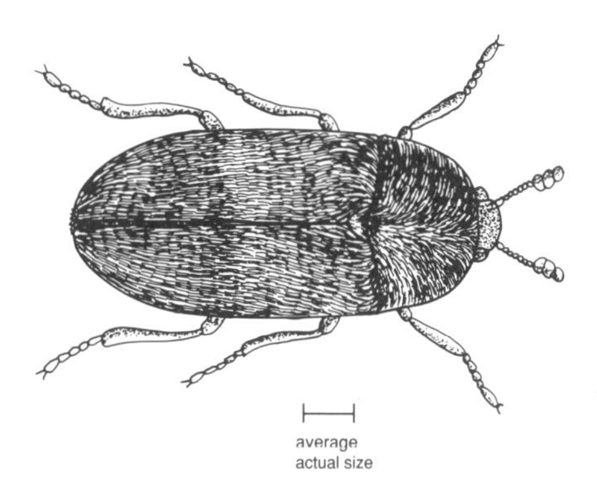

Typical Dermestid beetle — adult (from above)

Larva Up to 15 mm long, light brown. Three pairs of legs (H). Very obvious transverse bands of dark hairs along body. Two spines on rear end (H). Found on food source but may disperse some distance before boring refuge tunnels in timber or other soft material.

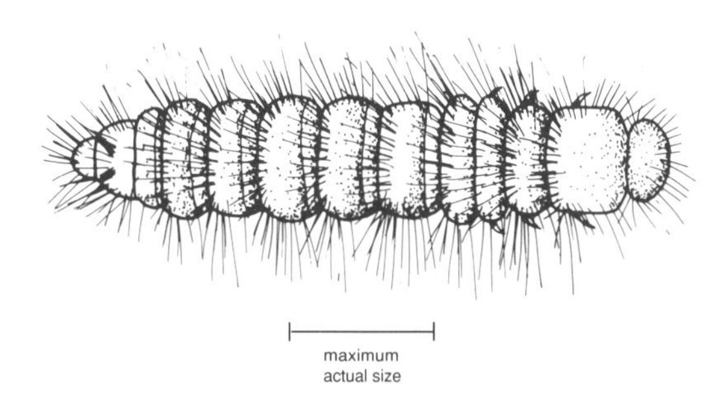

Typical Dermestid beetle — larva (from above)

Wood wasps

Latin names: *Urocerus (Sirex) gigas* and other species of family Siricidae

Habitat Softwoods. Attacks unhealthy trees and newly felled logs. Damage may be incorporated into buildings and larvae may survive to emerge as adults later but cannot reinfest dry timber.

Damage characteristics:
Emergence holes Large, circular, 4 – 7 mm diameter.
Tunnels Precisely circular, 4 – 7 mm diameter. May be exposed longitudinally during sawing or planing resulting in oval appearance which may be confused with longhorn damage. Not easily seen during handling because of densely packed bore dust.
Bore dust Coarse, densely packed; cannot be shaken out.
Likely mis-identifications Deathwatch beetle, page 65; Bostrychid powderpost beetle, page 94; house longhorn beetle, page 62; forest longhorn beetle, page 88; Tenebrionid beetle, page 76; bees or wasps, page 71; marine borer, page 99.

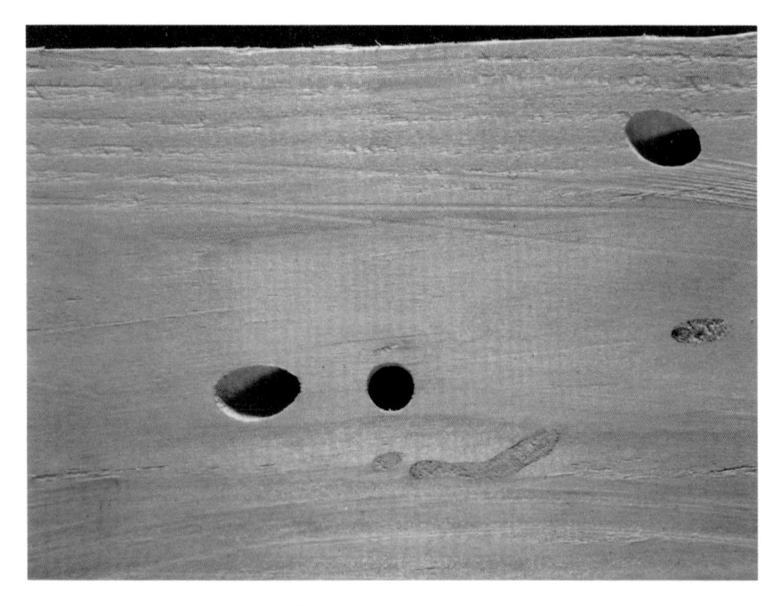

Wood wasp — damaged wood (actual size)

Remedial treatment None necessary. All adults should emerge within 12 months of drying. Reinfestation not possible.

Insect characteristics and location:
Adult Usually identified from other wasps by large size (18 – 35 mm), narrow body and conspicuous yellow patch behind each eye (H). Female has long spine-like projection on rear of body used for egg laying. Dwarf adults may be produced if drying occurs during larval stage. May occasionally emerge from new timbers in buildings or from firewood.

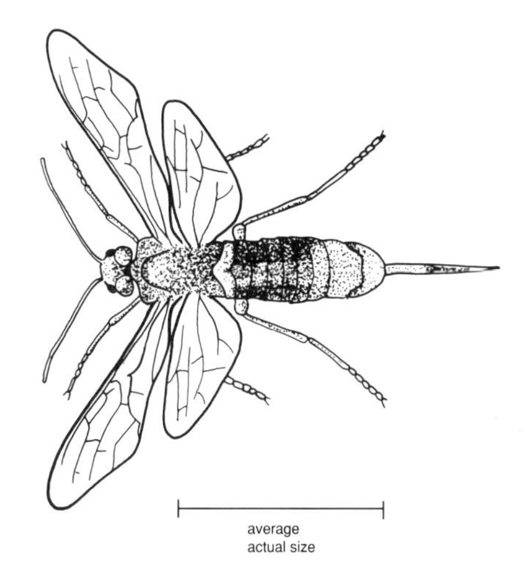

Typical wood wasp — adult (from above)

Larva Up to 30 mm, straight, cylindrical, pale cream. Dark spine on rear end (H). Markedly segmented. Three pairs of legs (H). Occasionally found in timber.

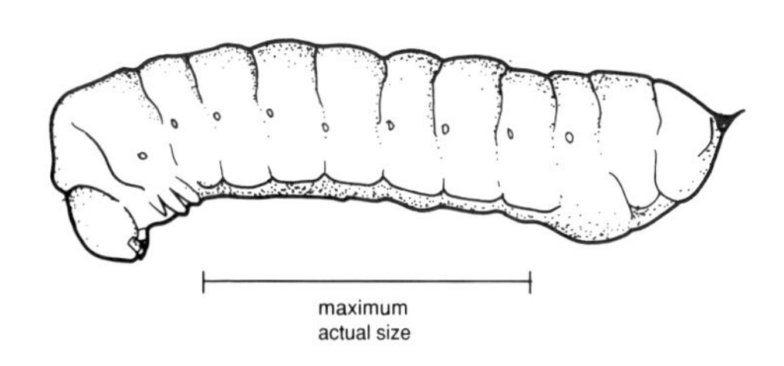

Typical wood wasp — larva (from the side)

Bostrychid powderpost beetles

Latin name: family Bostrychidae — many species

Habitat Partially or fully dried sapwood of tropical timber and plywood, sometimes bamboo and cane. Only found in imported timber in UK. Larvae may survive for some months and often emerge as adults. Cannot reinfest in UK climatic conditions, either outside or in heated buildings.

Damage characteristics:
General Adults bore into wood to lay eggs, therefore bore holes do not necessarily indicate emergence.
Emergence and entry holes Circular, 3 – 6 mm diameter.
Tunnels Circular, 3 – 6 mm diameter, convoluted, ending in pupal chambers near surface.
Bore dust Fine, talc-like, cream coloured. Tightly packed in tunnels.
Likely mis-identifications Lyctus powderpost beetle, page 60; deathwatch beetle, page 65; house longhorn beetle, page 62; wood wasp, page 92.

Remedial treatment Normally none necessary — infestations present when timber is imported will die out naturally without treatment, usually within 12 months. If treatment considered necessary to prevent further damage to valuable items before infestation dies out naturally, use organic solvent or paste.

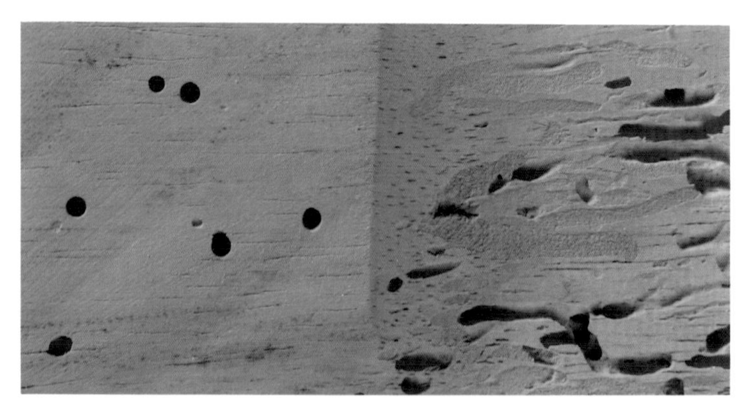

Bostrychid powderpost beetle — damaged wood (actual size) with surface partly planed to reveal tunnels

Insect characteristics and location:
Adult 4 – 11 mm long depending on species. Brown or black, cylindrical. Head not visible from above. Front of head usually flattened and heavily sculptured. Found on and around infested wood.

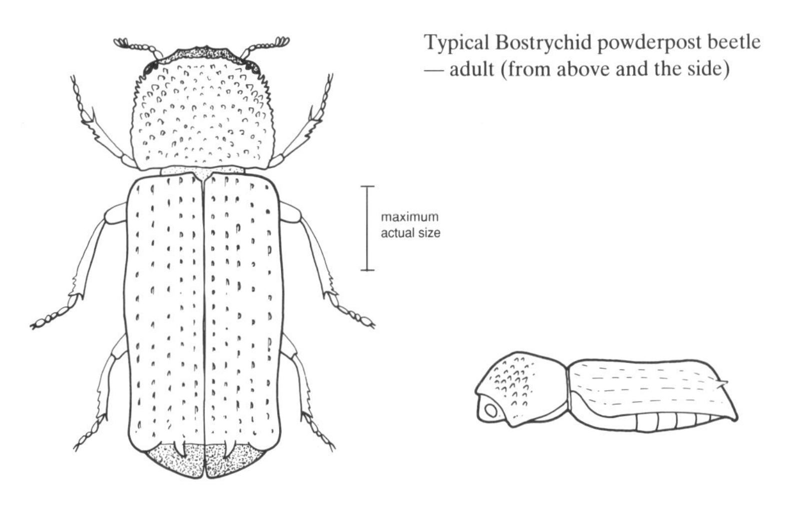

Typical Bostrychid powderpost beetle — adult (from above and the side)

Larva Up to 12 mm long, curved, pale cream. Three pairs of small legs (H). Several pairs of conspicuous oval breathing pores of uniform size along sides of abdomen (H). Diagonal raised white line on either side of body at head end (H). No enlarged breathing pores at rear end. Found in infested wood all year round.

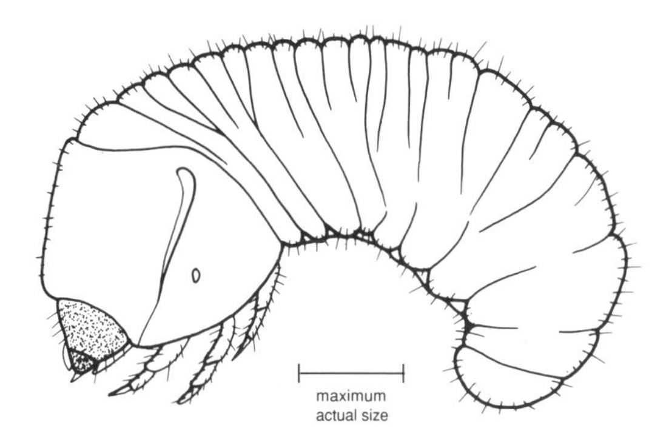

Typical Bostrychid powderpost beetle — larva (from the side)

Jewel beetles

Latin name: family Buprestidae — few species

Habitat Standing trees. Damaged timber may be incorporated into buildings. Commonest in imported north American softwoods including western red cedar. Some larvae may survive drying and emerge as adults later but cannot reinfest dried timber. Records suggest that larvae of some species can survive for over 20 years in dry timber and emerge as adults many years after installation in buildings.

Damage characteristics:
Emergence holes Few. Large, oval, 7 – 8 mm across at widest dimension.
Tunnels Flattened oval or kidney shaped, 7 – 8 mm diameter. Rarely joining up.
Bore dust Sausage-shaped pellets (H) densely packed in tunnels.
Likely mis-identifications House longhorn beetle, page 62; forest longhorn beetle, page 88.

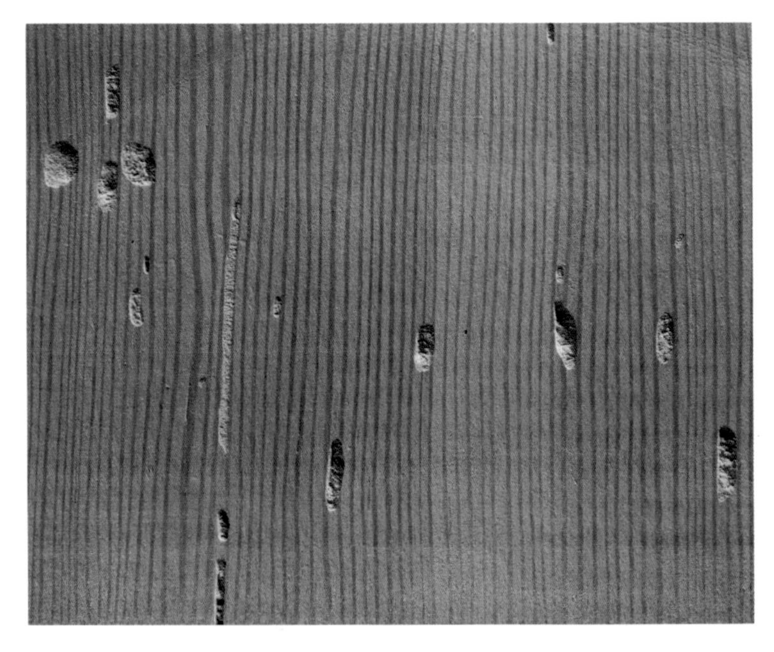

Jewel beetle — damaged wood (actual size)

Remedial treatment None necessary, although affected visible timbers may have to be replaced because of unsightliness of damage.

Insect characteristics and location:
Adult Large, flattened, (typically 11 – 20 mm long though in rare cases up to 65 mm). Commonest species are a distinctive bright metallic green. Occasionally found on and around timber.

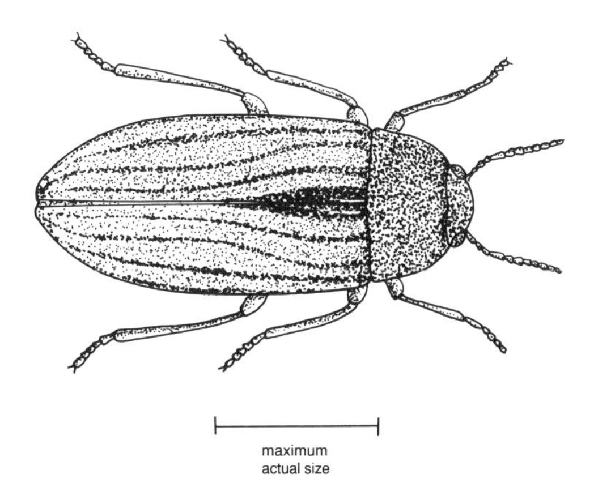

Typical jewel beetle — adult (from above)

Larva Up to 35 mm long, straight, pale cream. No legs. Distinctive large flat head. Rarely found in building timbers.

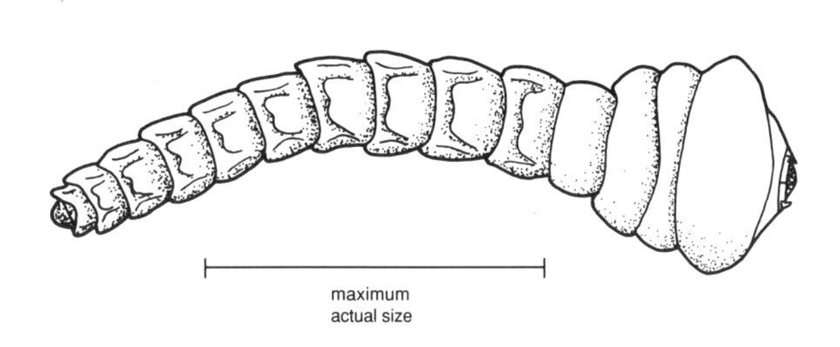

Typical jewel beetle — larva (from above)

Pinhole borer beetles

Latin names: families Platypodidae, Scolytidae and Lymexylidae — many species
Other names: ambrosia beetle and shothole borer

Habitat Softwoods and hardwoods, particularly tropical timbers. Attacks standing trees and felled green timber. Infestation dies out when timber is dried. Insect cannot reinfest dried timber even if this becomes damp at a later date. Damaged timber may be incorporated into buildings or used in plywood manufacture, but unimportant unless aesthetically unacceptable.

Damage characteristics:
Entry holes Circular, 1 – 2 mm diameter, but rarely seen in sawn timber.
Tunnels At right angles to grain direction. Empty, straight and unbranched or with several very short lateral chambers. Usually darkly stained. Staining may extend into wood around tunnel.
Bore dust None, but sawdust may become impacted into tunnels during sawing of infested timber.
Likely mis-identifications Common furniture beetle, page 57; Lyctus powderpost beetle, page 60; bark borer beetle, page 81; Ptilinus beetle, page 68; sawfly, page 86; moth, page 84.

Remedial treatment None necessary. NOTE: larvae and adults are very rarely found — their life cycles are usually completed before timber is dry.

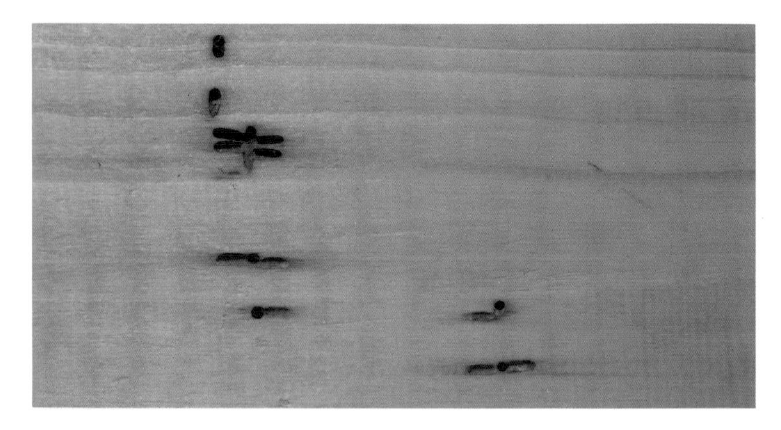

Pinhole borer beetle — damaged wood (actual size)

Marine borers

Latin name: *Teredo* spp
Other name: shipworm

Habitat A mollusc which attacks logs floated in marine waters before sawing. Damage is included here because, although the mollusc dies when the log is removed from water for sawing, its tunnels can be mistaken for attack by wood-boring insects if damaged timber is incorporated into buildings.

Damage characteristics:
General Single blind-ending tunnels, precisely circular, up to 300 mm long and 15 mm diameter. Actual size depends on species and state of maturity. Sectioned tunnels may be mistaken for emergence holes of wood-boring beetles, but can be identified by the lack of bore dust and the chalky white calcareous tunnel linings.
Likely mis-identification Deathwatch beetle, page 65; wood wasp, page 92.

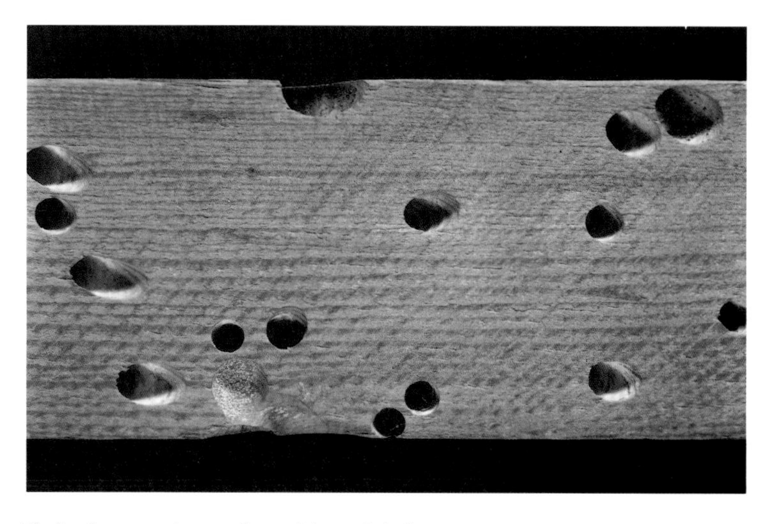

Marine borer — damaged wood (actual size)

Remedial treatment of damage by wood-boring insects[2]

- ❑ Identify the insect.

- ❑ If the damage is caused by those species which fall within damage category A (insecticidal treatment usually needed), try to determine whether the infestation is active or not. Fresh exit holes, often in large numbers, and bore dust on or below the timber are signs of an active infestation. Vibrations may, though, dislodge bore dust from extinct infestations.

- ❑ If damage is associated with fungal decay (damage category B and deathwatch beetle), check for dampness and carry out necessary remedial measures for dealing with fungal decay (see pages 19 and 35)[8, 9, 10].

- ❑ If the infestation is thought to be active, estimate the significance of the damage. More than 20 holes per 100 mm run of timber can be considered as a severe attack but far fewer holes may be significant for the house longhorn or deathwatch beetles.

- ❑ If structural timbers are affected, carry out or arrange a full survey to determine whether structural repairs are necessary and, if they are, take appropriate steps to secure structural integrity[7].

- ❑ Decide on the type and extent of remedial treatment most suitable for the particular insect and the type of component damaged[14–16]. Further recommendations for treatments for the different wood-boring insects are given within the details for each insect type.

Non-wood-boring insects commonly found in buildings

There are many insects which live in buildings, feeding on a variety of food sources present, or which may enter buildings accidentally. They can often be mistaken for wood-boring insects and may even be found in old emergence holes. While there are many insects which may be found occasionally, those listed below are found more commonly. The references to actual size in the captions to the figures on the next two pages relate to body length only (ie, excluding appendages such as legs and antennae).

Insect	**Common origin**	**Remedial measure**
Biscuit beetle *(Stegobium paniceum)*	Stored dry food of flour origin (biscuit, flour, meal)[20]	Dispose of infested items
Dermestids: eg, carpet beetle, larder beetle, hide beetle	Dry animal matter, often birds nests in lofts, disused flues and dead mice	Dispose of infested matter
Plaster beetle, book lice (Psocids)	Mould and certain food products such as flour and yeast	Clean and sterilise mould-affected surfaces Dispose of infested foods. Reduce humidity and condensation
Garden weevils	Often overwinter in buildings or are brought in with firewood	Not necessary
Wood lice	Large numbers suggest excessive damp. Small numbers may intrude	Check for dampness and keep vegetation clear of external walls
Spider beetles (Ptinids)	Dry animal and vegetable matter. Birds nests. Neglected packaged food	Dispose of infested material
Mealworm beetle *(Tenebrio mollitor)*	Cereal products, but occasionally very decayed damp wood	Dispose of infested material. Remove decayed wood
Silver fish	Damp organic material and detritus	Ventilate and dry building
Masonry (mortar) bees	Bore holes in exterior soft mortar and stone	Fill holes with a harder mortar

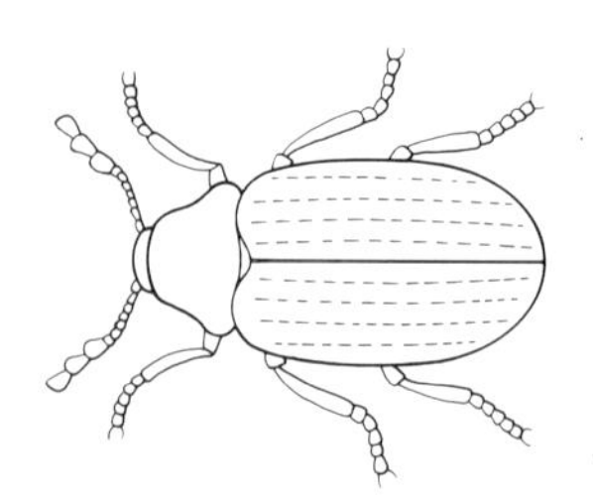 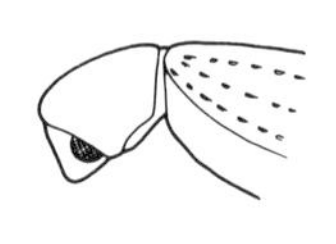 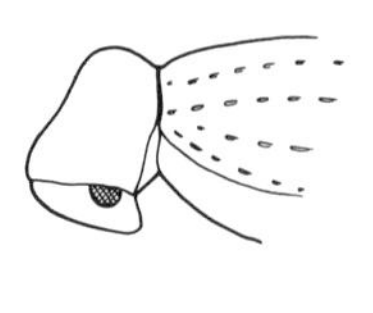

Stegobium paniceum — biscuit beetle (above left, actual size 3 mm). Easily confused with common furniture beetle due to similar shape and colouring. Main difference between them is shown in the side views of their heads: biscuit beetle (above centre) and common furniture beetle (above right)

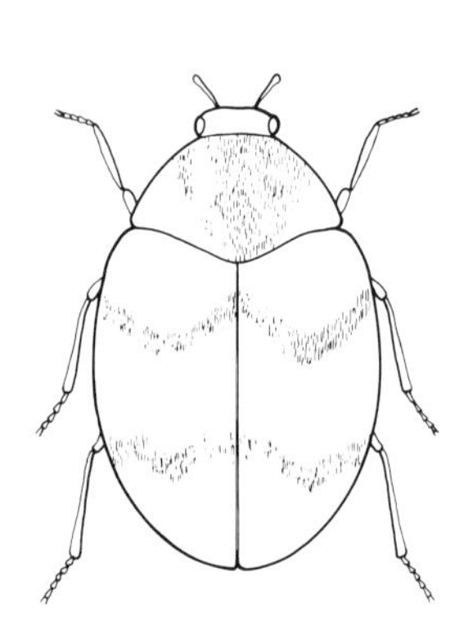

Anthrenus spp — carpet beetle (actual size 3 mm)

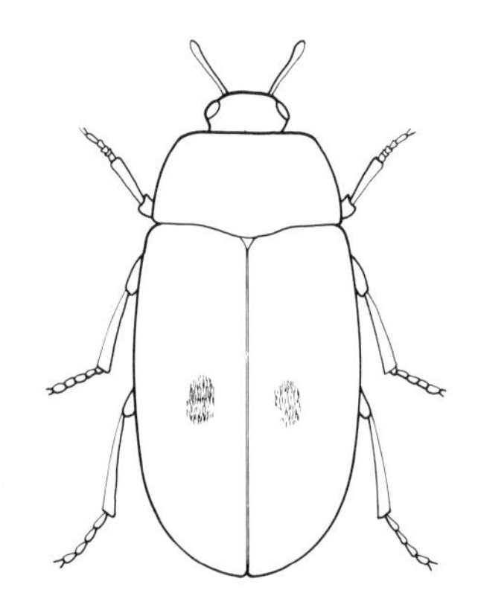

Attagenus pellio — two-spotted carpet beetle (actual size 6 mm)

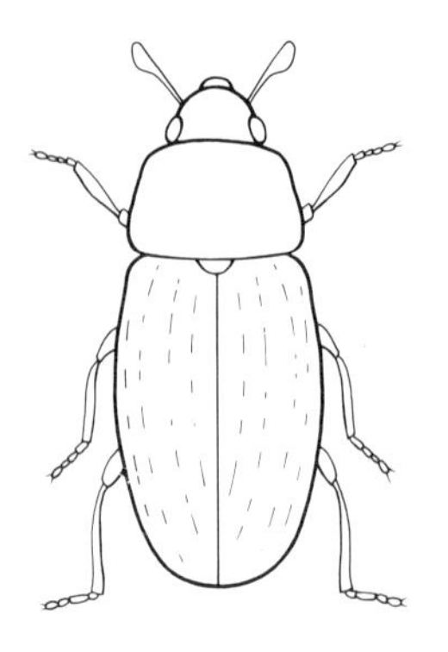

Mycetophagus spp — plaster beetle (actual size 2 mm)

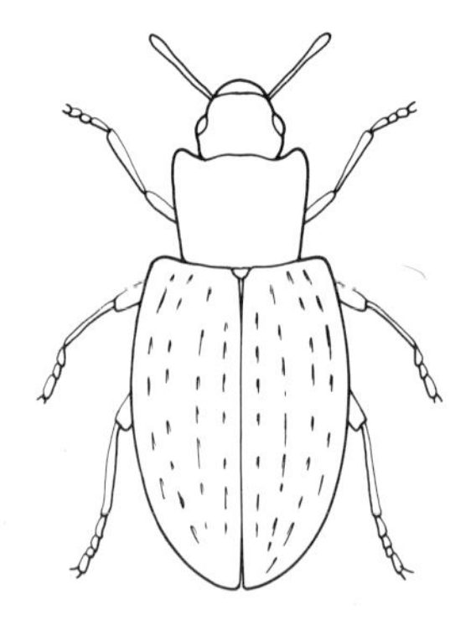

Lathridius spp — plaster beetle (actual size 4 mm)

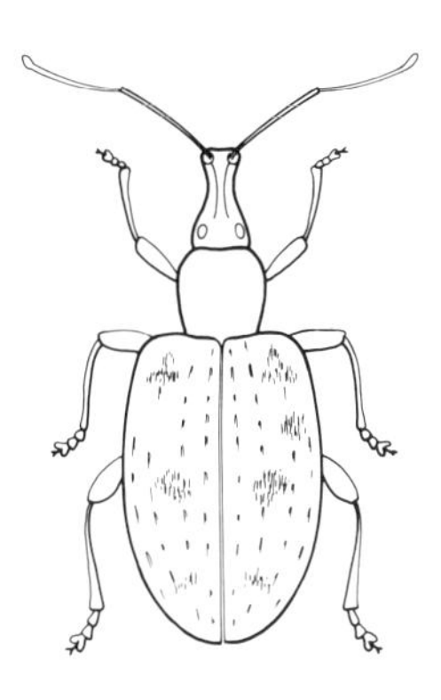

Otiorrhynchus sulcatus — garden weevil
(actual size 12 mm)

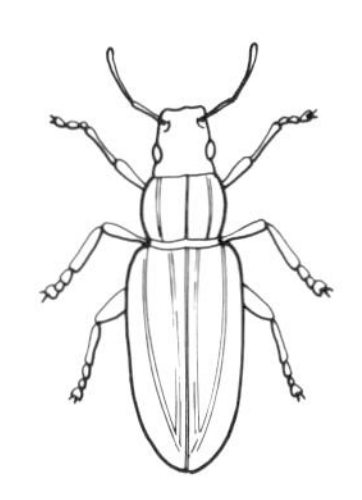

Sitona spp — garden weevil
(actual size 5 mm)

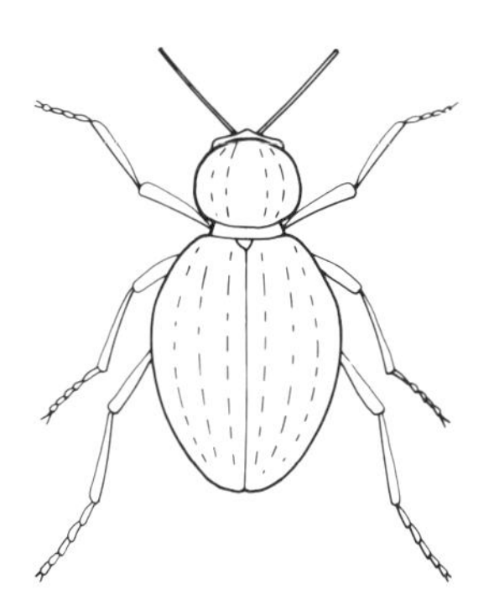

Ptinus spp — spider beetle
(actual size 3 mm)

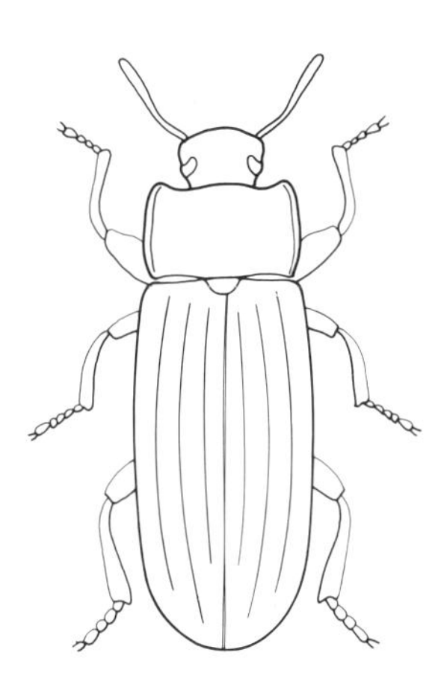

Tenebrio mollitor — mealworm
beetle (actual size 16 mm)

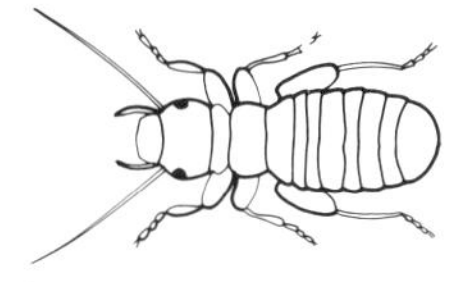

Psocid — book louse (up to 1 mm)

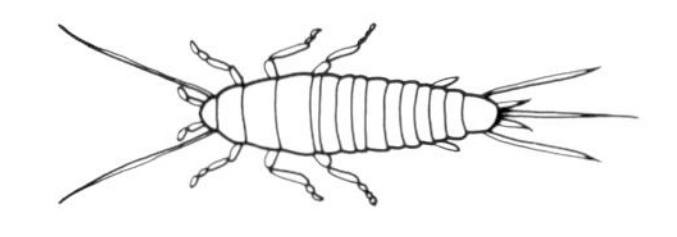

Silver fish (up to 12 mm)

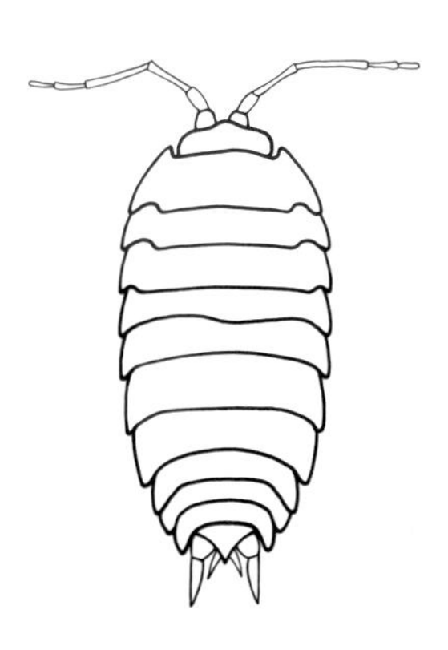

Wood louse (up to 15 mm)

Appendix A Types of preservatives and methods of application for pretreatment of wood

A range of preservatives of the types shown below are available for pretreatment of wood. Only those commercial products cleared as safe for use under the Control of Pesticides Regulations 1986 should be used. British Standards give details of treatments and their suitability for different situations.

The specific fungicides and insecticides are subject to regular review by the Health and Safety Executive. From time to time products are withdrawn and new active ingredients introduced. It is important, therefore, to establish that a product has current approval.

Preservative type	Treatment methods
Tar oils:	
Coal tar creosote to BS 144 Parts 1 and 2	Pressure, open tank, immersion or brush
Solutions of one or more fungicides or insecticides in an organic solvent, usually petroleum oil distillate	Double vacuum, immersion, deluging, brush or spray
Water borne:	
Copper-chromium-arsenic to BS 4072 Parts 1 and 2	Pressure
Disodium octaborate	Diffusion

Appendix B Remedial treatments for eradicating fungi and insects

Organic solvent liquids
White spirit or similar solvent carriers containing insecticide or fungicide or both. Applied by brushing or spraying but may be pressure injected into large timbers. Painted or varnished items must be stripped before treatment.

Emulsion liquids
Water-oil emulsions containing insecticide or fungicide or both. Usually made up on site by mixing concentrate with water. Applied by spray. Not suitable for injection. Same preparation for painted or varnished items as with organic solvent liquids. Normally used only for common furniture beetle treatment due to limited penetration[16].

Pastes
Water-based pastes or bodied emulsions (mayonnaise) containing insecticide or fungicide or both. Applied by palette knife or caulking gun. May be injected into cavities. Higher surface loadings and deeper penetration possible than with liquids. Labour intensive application normally restricts use to large components or structurally important timbers.

Smokes
Canisters containing pyrotechnic formulation and insecticide[14]. When ignited produce a cloud of insecticide particles which deposit on all surfaces. Used to kill adult beetles. The low persistence of the deposits necessitates repeated annual treatments in order to reduce or eradicate an infestation. Particularly useful for controlling deathwatch beetle in structures which would otherwise be difficult or expensive to treat[15].

Dichlorvos strips
Plastic strips which gradually release insecticide (dichlorvos) vapour into the air[14]. Will kill emerging adults of the common furniture beetle when strips installed prior to emergence season. Annual renewal of strips required in order to reduce or eradicate an infestation. Normally effective only in roof spaces with under-tile-or-slate felt lining.

Surface biocides
Water-based solutions of fungicides. Applied by injection or surface spraying of masonry. Used to provide a fungicidal barrier to the spread of dry rot[9, 10].

Fungicidal rods, plugs and tablets
Solid, moulded forms of water soluble fungicide. Applied by insertion into pre-drilled masonry and window joinery[13, 21]. Used to provide a fungicidal zone by diffusion into moisture present in the substrate.

Fungicidal renderings
Applied to the surface of damp walls to provide a fungicidal barrier to the spread of dry rot[22].

NOTE: portable items of high value (eg, antiques) can be sterilised by specialist treatment using gas fumigation.

Appendix C Health and safety aspects of remedial treatments

Because some chemicals used in remedial treatments are harmful to mammals and other living creatures to some extent, while some also present a fire hazard, there are Codes of Practice governing the use of these materials[23, 24]. In the interests of environmental safety they should not be used unnecessarily. Use only products cleared under the Control of Pesticides Regulations 1986.

Summary of hazards and precautions*

Hazard	Typical precautions
To operatives	Wear safety equipment (eg, gloves, overalls, boots, headgear and goggles). Ventilate premises during treatment. Use appropriate respiratory protection. Apply barrier cream to skin. Prohibit eating, drinking and smoking in treatment area. Wash hands before eating and smoking.Wash off any fluid coming into contact with skin IMMEDIATELY. Bath or shower at the end of the day. Launder protective clothing regularly.
To occupants	Cover water tanks and ensure no contamination of foodstuffs can occur. Restrict access to freshly treated areas, particularly by children and pets for a minimum of 48 hours. Ensure premises are well ventilated.
Fire	Isolate electric circuits†. Keep reserves of treatment fluid outdoors. Do not allow smoking in a treatment area or its immediate vicinity. Extinguish pilot lights. Protect light bulbs. Ventilate area very well.
Environmental	Dispose of empty containers and other contaminated wastes correctly (seek advice if necessary). Use coarse spray to minimise aerosol formulation and unnecessary dispersion of pesticide. There are special regulations in existence regarding the treatment of roof spaces which are roosting sites for bats. Information on surveying roofs for bats and the permitted treatments is available from nature conservation organisations such as English Nature[17].

*** The Control of Pesticides Regulations places a legal requirement on users to comply in full with the instructions contained in the product label.**

† Organic solvent fluids should not be brought into contact with PVC cables as they can cause embrittlement and leaching of plasticiser which may drip into switches and ceiling roses.

Glossary

Abdomen Rear end of an insect's body

Active Live insects or growing fungus present

Adult Last stage of an insect's life cycle during which it is capable of reproduction

Antenna Jointed feeler on head of an insect

Blue stain Sap stain in which discolouration is bluish

Blue stain in service Staining of timber in service by blue stain fungi

Bore dust Excreted pellets and dust, and woody tissue fragments produced by wood-boring insects

Bracket Fruit-body growing at right angles to a vertical surface

Breathing pore See Pore

Brown rot Rot caused by wood-destroying fungi which digest cellulose leaving a brown friable residue of lignin

Cell (1) Chamber excavated in wood by an insect in which eggs are laid and larvae develop
(2) A unit of which plants and animals are composed

Detritus Very small pieces of dead and decomposing organic material

Dry rot Brown rot caused by the fungus *Serpula lacrymans*

Emergence hole Hole made by adult insect on its emergence from infested wood

Emergence period Time of year during which adult wood-boring insects develop and emerge from infested wood

Entry hole Hole made by some adult insects to enter and lay eggs within wood

Eye spot Small, darkly pigmented spot on head of insect larva

Fruit-body Spore-bearing structure produced by fungi

Gill Thin plate-like structure on mushroom-like fruit-body, on which spores are produced

Head Front section of an insect's body, carrying mouth parts and antennae

Hypha A microscopic thread, many of which form the vegetative part (mycelium) and the reproductive part (fruit-body) of a fungus

Inactive Infestation or infection of wood in which no live insects or actively growing fungi are present

Infection	Invasion of wood by fungi or other micro-organisms
Infestation	Establishment of wood-boring insect activity in wood
Larva	Immature, feeding, grub-like stage of insect life cycle
Latent	Fungus which is live but not growing, although capable of further growth and damage to wood if suitable conditions occur
Mature	(1) Adult stage of insect life cycle (2) Stage at which a fruit-body produces ripe spores
Mould	Superficial growth caused by non-wood-rotting fungi
Mycelium	A sheet or network of microscopic threads (hyphae) of a decay fungus which grows over and through wood under attack
Pit	A small depression in a surface
Plate	A fruit-body lying flat on a surface
Plaster fungi	A group of non-wood-destroying fungi producing large fruit-bodies, which may be found on damp plaster, brickwork, etc
Pore	(1) Minute opening in the end of a tube-like structure in a fruit-body through which spores are released (2) Breathing organ in an insect larva
Pupa	Stage in insect life cycle during which change from larva to adult occurs
Sap stain	Discolouration of sapwood of timber (principally green timber) resulting from the growth of fungi which invade wood cells and digest the contents
Slime moulds	Group of fungi, otherwise known as *Myxomycetes*, which feed on bacteria within wet wood but fruit on the wood surface
Snout	Elongated extension to front of head of an insect
Soft rot	Superficial wet rot caused by micro-fungi
Spore	A one or several-celled very small reproductive body produced by a fungus
Strand	An aggregation of hyphae which has the ability to transport food and water
Thorax	Middle section of an insect's body carrying the legs, wings and wing covers
Wet rot	Rot caused by wood-rotting fungi (other than *Serpula lacrymans*) which characteristically attack comparatively wet timber in buildings
White rot	Rot caused by wood-rotting fungi which digest both cellulose and lignin, and generally lighten the colour of wood

Index to common and Latin names of fungi and insects

References

1 **Building Research Establishment.** Timbers: their natural durability and resistance to preservative treatment. *BRE Digest* 296. Garston, BRE, 1985.

2 **Berry R W and Takens-Milne E.** Remedial treatment of wood rot and insect attack in buildings. Garston, Building Research Establishment, 1993.

3 **Building Research Establishment.** House inspection for dampness: a first step to remedial treatment for wood rot. *BRE Information Paper* IP 19/88. Garston, BRE, 1988.

4 **Building Research Establishment.** Rising damp in walls: diagnosis and treatment. *BRE Digest* 245. Garston, BRE, 1986.

5 **Oxley T A and Gobert E G.** Dampness in buildings. Sevenoaks, Butterworth, 1983.

6 **Garratt J and Nowak F.** Tackling condensation. BRE Report. Garston, BRE, 1991.

7 **Staveley H S and Glover P.** Building surveys. London, Butterworth-Heinemann, 1990.

8 **Building Research Establishment.** Wet rots: recognition and control. *BRE Digest* 345. Garston, BRE, 1989.

9 **Jenning D H and Bravery A F (editors).** *Serpula lacrymans.* Fundamental biology and control strategies. Chichester, Wiley & Sons (Publishers), 1991.

10 **Building Research Establishment.** Dry rot: its recognition and control. *BRE Digest* 299. Garston, BRE, 1989.

11 **Bravery A F.** Mould and its control. *Building Research Establishment Information Paper* IP11/85. Garston, BRE, 1985.

12 **Carey J K.** Blue staining of timber in service: its cause, prevention and treatment. *Building Research Establishment Information Paper* IP9/91. Garston, BRE, 1991.

13 **Carey J K.** In-situ treatment of exterior joinery using boron-based implants. *Building Research Establishment Information Paper* IP14/91. Garston, BRE, 1991.

14 **Building Research Establishment.** Insecticidal treatments against wood-boring insects. *BRE Digest* 327. Garston, BRE, 1987.

15 **Read S J.** Controlling death watch beetle. *Building Research Establishment Information Paper* IP19/86. Garston, BRE, 1986.

16 **Berry R W and Orsler R J.** Emulsion-based formulations for remedial treatments against woodworm. *Building Research Establishment Information Paper* IP15/83. Garston, BRE, 1983.

17 **English Nature.** Bats in roofs — a guide for surveyors. Peterborough, English Nature, 1985.

18 **Building Research Establishment.** Control of lichens, moulds and similar growths. *BRE Digest* 370. Garston, BRE, 1992.

19 **Hickin N E.** The insect factor in wood decay. London, Hutchinson & Co (Publishers) Ltd, 1975.

20 **British Museum (Natural History).** Common insect pests of stored food products. *Economic Series* No 15. London, Trustees of the British Museum, 1980.

21 **Lea R G.** In situ treatment for existing window joinery. *Building Research Establishment Information Paper* IP21/81. Garston, BRE, 1981.

22 **Preservation Centre for Wood.** Fungicidal plaster. 24 Ossory Road, London, SE1.

23 **British Wood Preserving and Damp-proofing Association.** Code of practice for remedial treatment. Stratford, BWPDA, 1983.

24 **Health and Safety Executive and Department of the Environment.** Remedial timber treatment in buildings. A guide to good practice and the safe use of wood preservatives. London, HMSO, 1991.

BRE publications are available from BRE Bookshop, Building Research Establishment, Garston, Watford, WD2 7JR. A free list of BRE publications is available on request.

Typical adult sizes for common wood-boring beetles

House longhorn beetle	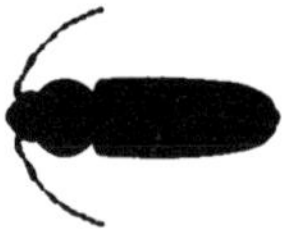 (range 10 – 20 mm)
Jewel beetle	(range 11 – 20 mm, in rare cases up to 65 mm)
Bostrychid powderpost beetle	(range 4 – 11 mm)
Deathwatch beetle	(range 6 – 9 mm)
Dermestid beetle	 (range 4 – 7 mm)
Lyctus powderpost beetle	(range 4 – 7 mm)
Ptilinus beetle	(range 4 – 6 mm)
Bark borer beetle	(range 4 – 6 mm)
Common furniture beetle	(range 3 – 5 mm)
Wood-boring weevil	(range 3 – 5 mm)

* Figures are for length in each case